WITH A TASK BEFORE ME

BOOKS BY VIRGINIA S. EIFERT

THREE RIVERS SOUTH
A Story of Young Abe Lincoln

THE BUFFALO TRACE
The Story of Abraham Lincoln's Ancestors

OUT OF THE WILDERNESS
Young Abe Lincoln Grows Up

WITH A TASK BEFORE ME
Abraham Lincoln Leaves Springfield

MISSISSIPPI CALLING

"I NOW LEAVE, NOT KNOWING WHEN, OR WHETHER EVER, I MAY RETURN ... WITH A TASK BEFORE ME GREATER THAN THAT WHICH RESTED UPON WASHINGTON."

WITH A
TASK BEFORE ME

Abraham Lincoln Leaves Springfield

BY

VIRGINIA S. EIFERT

ILLUSTRATED BY MANNING DE V. LEE

DODD, MEAD & COMPANY · NEW YORK · 1958

ILLUSTRATIONS

CHAPTER ONE

THE SPRING NIGHT was warm around him, scented with blossoms and alive with the small sounds of wild things abroad in the moonlight. And over the leafing trees and the crab-apple flowers, over the men huddled close to their campfires, fear laid its uneasy grip.

Captain Abraham Lincoln sat with his long arms wrapped around his legs, knees hunched to his chin, and stared into the leaping flames. Around him, other fires cast their ruddy glow upon the log fort, upon the sober faces of several hundred volunteer soldiers. He and his men said little. They were talked out, joked out, worn out.

They had been together since the end of April, 1832, when Governor Reynolds had called for the militia to protect citizens from the attacks of Black Hawk and his Sac Indian warriors, who were spreading terror throughout northern Illinois. But the eager militia had seen no action, no fighting, no Indians.

By the night of May 14, the men were sick of each other's company; disgusted with the errand which had sent them slogging through swamps; weary of sleeping in flimsy tents; cooking poor food over a smoky fire; enduring a rainy spring. They were sick of this war in which they were forever chasing after Indians they never saw and never had a chance to fight.

Now, gathered around the evening campfires at Fort Dixon, beside the Rock River, on one of the first really fine nights since the beginning of the Black Hawk War, the men were silenced under the clammy hand of fear. Although the gleaming white moon and

1

the fragrant night and the glittering river were all so sweet, so placid and so still, the men knew that something sinister was near, and they were afraid.

Lincoln himself was worried. Things were too quiet. Just listening to the silence of the hills and the stars and watching that uncanny, all-seeing moon made a small chill creep along his spine and set up an unexplained faster beating of his heart. Action, actual combat even, would certainly be better than this terrible waiting, this not knowing what was going to happen, this ignorance of what might be happening at that very moment to Major Stillman and his soldiers.

Major Isaiah Stillman and a company of men had set off from the main body of troops, with only four days' provisions, in a hope of locating the Indians and surprising them—as if anyone could surprise Black Hawk and his evil Winnebago associate, Wabo-kie-shiek, who was called the Prophet! This was Black Hawk's home country. He always seemed to know where the white men were; always contrived to leave clues and signs as to where the Indians could be found; and then, when the eager soldiers wearily arrived, the prey had neatly vanished, but always left new depredations behind.

It had been so ever since Black Hawk, the thin, Oriental-looking war leader of the Sacs, in April, 1832, had crossed the Mississippi back into Illinois from Iowa, whence he had been banished the year before. He had been harassing the settlers, burning a house or barn here, killing a man or stealing a horse there, then slipping away before he and his people were caught.

Black Hawk was never a chief but he had conspired to make trouble wherever he went. He had gathered around him other warring Indians and had worked with the British to fight the Americans during the War of 1812. He had never lost his hatred for the people who had usurped his land. Even though the United States Government had made fair treaties with the Sacs, and their annuities were generous and prompt, Black Hawk hated all Americans.

At Fort Dixon, the silence was growing quite unbearable

2

around the campfires. Songs which one or another of the men attempted died of sheer lack of enthusiasm. A dog barked far off and another answered, baying the moon. There was an owl calling somewhere in the trees along the glittering river. A sharp splash in the water alerted every man in the camp, and the pacing sentries, muskets ready, whirled toward the sound. Heads turned, necks stiffened, the small talk which had risen froze on lips.

But it was only a beaver. The soldiers could see its dark head cleaving the water, the moonlight silvering the triangular wake trailing behind.

Abraham Lincoln stood up. He stretched tall above his companions.

"Well, I reckon it's about time to turn in, men," he said casually, though he was not feeling at all casual. "If you can get Job Ramshaw here pried off his blanket and his trumpet warmed up, maybe he can give us a bugle call to officially end the day."

"Don't you figure a bugle call would just attract attention to our camp, Lincoln?" asked Travice Elmore timidly. He had been hearing things all evening. "You can't tell how close them redskins are to us this minute!"

"From what I've heard," said Lincoln grimly, still standing tall, hands on hips, "Black Hawk knows exactly where we are at all times, and a bugle tootling isn't going to tell him a thing. Go ahead, Job; maybe it'll give us a little courage to last until morning!"

But the bugle call was mournful, and it cracked in the wrong places. Job Ramshaw was scared. He couldn't tongue his notes right; his lips felt dry and stiff; he gave up. In silence, the men made ready to crawl into their tents and blankets. Watchful and jittery, the sentries paced.

Abraham Lincoln could see Major Buckmaster in his tent, writing by candlelight, noted how he often raised his head sharply, as if listening, and knew that he, too, was uneasy. Long after the others had finally gone to sleep and Major Buckmaster's candle was out, the dogs still bayed the great white moon of May, the river still glittered, the beaver still splashed, and Lincoln lay wide-awake.

3

The Indians were up to something. He knew it as well as if they had told him themselves. Black Hawk was near, probably nearer than anyone dreamed, yet there was no sign of anything nor any suspicious noise or movement—but then, the Indians wouldn't be noisy or give away their presence until they were ready to attack. They would stealthily surround the camp, then charge upon the unprepared soldiers. And then it would be too late.

The thought was chilling. Lincoln remembered stories his father had told of the old days in Kentucky when folk were afraid to sleep at night because of the Shawnees and their terrible raids. He had thought that 1832 was far too distant from those frontier days in the wilderness for the settlers to have need to dread the Indians ever again. Men today, he felt, didn't seem to be as hardy as they must have been in the more demanding past. They got scared more easily.

Look at his own bunch, nervous as so many old women, homesick and complaining, afraid to go to sleep, afraid to walk behind the rocks for fear of Indians lurking and too cowardly to go and rout them out if they were there—well, not all his men. He had plenty of good, brave fellows, he was sure, but a lot of them didn't hold up so well in the face of suspense. Look at himself, jittery as a cat and for no reason.

The owl called again, closer now, and he saw the dark shadow of soundless wings flit across the moonlight and vanish in a clump of trees. He wished morning would come. Moonlight was too mysterious for comfort, with all its glints and shadows and the strange bits of unidentified, detached sound which seem to be part of such a spring night. He tried to sleep, but it was no use. Something was going to happen. He could feel it, but he didn't know what. . . .

But night passed. It was morning at last, a May day singing with birds, fresh and fragrant and sparkling, as if evil could never exist in the lovely Rock River country. Job Ramshaw blew his bugle with vigor.

Breakfast was almost over when there was a disorganized clumping of many horses and voices along the river trail. The men in

4

camp stopped what they were doing. Many paused in their eating, stood up, tense. Some reached for their guns.

Stillman's men appeared, wild-eyed, incoherent, torn, wounded, their horses lathered, dragging from exhaustion into camp. As Abraham Lincoln saw them coming, the terrible worries of the night before suddenly crystallized in certainty. It had happened. He had known, they had all sensed it, though they couldn't have told what it was nor where the menace lay. Black Hawk had struck again!

Some of the newcomers were babbling. Others were stonily silent. Their eyes did not focus, but seemed to be seeing with inner horror some distant scene.

"Injuns!" one gasped, staring, repeating over and over without expression, "Injuns! Run—run for—your lives! Run—for your lives! Run—"

The men in camp paled and some were about to take the words literally, when Major Buckmaster strode up, commanded order and demanded the details. Meanwhile, more men came straggling in, all coming from the direction Stillman's men had taken when they had set out cockily four days earlier, to rout out Black Hawk and his people, located to the north.

The soldiers were helped down from their trembling mounts, which had been whipped unmercifully and not permitted to rest along the trail. When they had been given food and drink, they were better able to relate what had happened.

"It was awful, I tell you!" one cried, tears running unheeded from his bloodshot eyes. "We was camped up along Sycamore Creek yesterday. The rain had finally stopped, and we was all so glad of that; it had been so wet we couldn't even have fires to cook our dinners. But with the rain over, we got fires goin' and was about to eat when suddenly, there was three Injuns right amongst us, like as if they'd sprung up out of the earth! How they'd got into the camp without nobody seein' them I do not know, but there they was, and one had a white flag. That didn't make no difference to us, though. They was Injuns, and right amongst us!

"Every man there was scared and didn't know what to do, and then someone commenced firin', and another did, too, and in the mess two of the Injuns was killed. The other got away, and as he pelted out of there in a gosh-awful hurry, somebody, I don't know who, spied a row of five Injuns on horseback on the rim of the hill. They was black against the sunset, watchin'."

"I was the one seen 'em first," another man put in. "And I tell you, them five scared us worse than the three!"

"Them five must've been spies," the other went on determinedly. "Anyways, them and the one that escaped must have gone on the double to tell Black Hawk, who sure wasn't far away. It wasn't till moonrise, though, that anything more happened.

"Then, suddenly, in the light of the moon, we seen a solid line of Injuns advancin' along the hill towards the camp! Somebody yelled 'Injuns!' and someone else piped up with 'run for your lives!' and that done it. All of a sudden, we was in a pure panic, runnin' every which-a-way, tramplin' down the ones that got in our path and a-screechin' and a-hollerin'!"

"We didn't have no chance to do much," put in another man, who had a bloody rag tied around his head. "The Injuns was on top of us, shootin' and tomahawkin'. Don't know how many they got; ain't took time to call the roll yet, I guess, but last I seen, there was men fallin' back there in the moonlight and Injuns everywhere!"

"Did an Injun hit you with his tommy-hawk? Did he try to scalp you, Billy?" asked one man, eying the bloody rag around the other's head.

"Naw, 'twasn't no Injun hit me," the other said, a trifle sheepishly. "I plumb rode agin a branch of a tree, back in the timber when I was a-clearin' out, and it like to knocked me off my horse. Cut a gash on my head, and I had to tie it up to keep the blood from runnin' into my eyes whilst I rode."

"Oh," said the other, and looked meaningfully from one to another of his companions who were listening to the recital of the ignominious retreat.

"So you cleared out and ran and didn't go back to see if you could help, eh?" put in Major Buckmaster quietly, but with an ugly gleam in his eye. "That was real brave and noble of you boys. How come you skinned out so fast? You got back here twice as quickly as you went out!"

Nobody said anything.

"And where is Major Stillman?" demanded Buckmaster. "Well, where is he?"

The silence grew more uncomfortable. One soldier, without any ado, keeled over in a faint, and the men let him lie where he fell.

Finally someone ventured, "Last I seen of him, he was in the midst of the fightin', with Injuns all around him."

"So you saved your worthless hides, and your commander could just take care of himself! If this was the regular army, you'd all be court-martialed and shot where you stand!"

Buckmaster was saved from doing violence by the appearance of Major Stillman himself and a group of the men who had stayed with him to the end. They were weary, bloody and speechless for a bit. Only their leader seemed to be in command of himself.

"Major," he said quietly to Buckmaster, "there's a bad mess left back there on the battlefield. I'd just as soon not go back there again. I've seen all I can take for a while, and my men, too—those who fought and lived to come back. I'd appreciate it if you'd detail a group to go out there and bury the dead, sir."

Abraham Lincoln and some of his company were chosen to go. In silence they rode up the valley and crossed the river to the battle-field, which now lay peaceful and sunny in the May daylight. A dozen men were sprawled where they had fallen . . . nine in the open meadow where last night's camp lay torn and disorganized; three in the woods. In silence, the burial crew went about their work. After the survivors had fled in panic, Black Hawk's men had taken their time and had decapitated or had scalped each one of the dead soldiers.

Abraham Lincoln felt deeply horrified. This was the real thing.

7

This was what his grandfather had known, back in the days when the Shawnees were the fear of all the settlers in Kentucky, the dread his grandmother had realized when she traveled the Wilderness Road and the Buffalo Trace to make a home in the dangerous country beyond the mountains. This was what the volunteer soldiers had not wanted to think or talk about when they joined the Illinois militia back in Sangamo Town and Athens and Springfield and New Salem.

Silently, Lincoln helped to bury the dead.

Less than a month before, when Governor Reynolds' proclamation was tacked on the wall of the post office in Sam Hill's store in New Salem, Illinois, sixty-eight men had enlisted from that community, to rid the state of Indians. A good many of the men entered the militia in a spirit of reckless and lighthearted bravado, more to break the monotony of a wet spring coming at the end of a long winter, than to be heroes.

"Let's make Lincoln captain and get up a company from here," proposed burly Jack Armstrong, one of Abe Lincoln's staunchest friends and supporters. "Who'll vote for Lincoln as captain?"

"Yay, yay, Abe Lincoln!" And at that moment it seemed like a fairly unanimous vote.

"Reminds me of the fox who asked all the chickens to vote for him, and it was a landslide in his favor," remarked Abraham drily. "You get a mighty unanimous vote that way. Knowing I could lick most of you in a fair fight, you probably figure you'd better vote yes—or else!"

"No, no!" protested George Spears. "You're our man, and a better captain we'd never find!"

"Well, we'll see," said the dubious new leader-elect.

It did not look quite so unanimous, however, next day at Richland, a few miles southwest of New Salem, in central Illinois, when the men from Clary's Clove, New Salem, Indian Point, Sugar Grove and Sangamo Town gathered to enlist. William Kirkpatrick, who owned a mill near the latter town, announced he would like the job of captain, had his own men signed up and was willing to get tough about it. He didn't fancy the way in which most of the crowd accepted Lincoln as leader, right off without any vote or anything.

"Say, Kirkpatrick," drawled Jack Armstrong, spitting a great arc of brown juice into the young pokeweeds. "We'd just about decided amongst us to have Abe Lincoln here for our captain. If you don't mind, we'd just as soon have him as someone else, namin' no names."

William Kirkpatrick flushed. He easily located Abraham Lincoln's broad shoulders looming above the others.

"Well," Kirkpatrick began coldly. "After all, I don't see why—"

"No, I reckon you don't," broke in Armstrong impatiently. "We don't want you for captain, Kirkpatrick, if I got to speak plain, because of the way you done treated Lincoln here when he did a job of work for you and you never paid him all he had comin' to him. We know your reputation!"

"Let's vote on it!" suggested young William Greene and Bill Berry together. The two were among Lincoln's best friends.

"How?"

"Lincoln stand here and Kirkpatrick there," said round-faced Billy Greene. "Now, whoever wants to fight under Lincoln, stand back of him, the others back of Kirkpatrick. The one with the longest tail to his kite gets the job!"

There was a considerable flurry of jostling and laughing, and when it was over, three-fourths of the men were standing in a long queue behind Abraham Lincoln, while a mere scattering stood uncomfortably behind William Kirkpatrick, who was thoroughly out of humor.

Jack Armstrong grinned at Abraham Lincoln. There was a strong majority look to the proceeding. It made Abraham feel remarkably good, warm, happy and somehow secure, to see how well liked he was and how his friends stood up for him. In politics, a pursuit he had planned to follow before the Black Hawk War came on and interrupted his high-flown notions, a vote like that would put him over the top at any election.

At the same time, he had a disagreeable, cold sort of feeling at the thought of how very little he knew about being an army officer and captaining a company of men. Nothing he had known in Indiana had fitted him for this, and very little of what he had read gave him an inkling of the procedure. He didn't know the first thing about issuing commands, and had his doubts, anyway, as to how the men would obey if he did find his voice and pipe up with an order.

He tried it out then, while he still had them lined up behind him.

"Company, fall in!" he shouted in his high-pitched voice, knocking his moccasined heels together and straightening up.

"Aw, go to the devil!" replied Pleasant Armstrong casually, and the men burst into a guffaw, slumping every which way and looking about as little like a troop of militia as any group of men Lincoln had ever seen. William Kirkpatrick laughed contemptuously.

"You'll see that you've picked up a panther by the tail, sir," he sneered, turning on his heel. "I wish you luck, but doubt if you'll have much!"

Abraham flushed. He squared about and towered over his men who were standing about or lounging on the grass, waiting to see what he would do.

"Company, attention!" he barked. There was no nonsense or indecision in his crisp voice. "Attention, I said," he snapped sternly, "and I mean it. I can lick every blamed one of you," he went on threateningly, "and I'll take on any man who can't get his backbone straightened up to stand at attention in my company. If we've got to go and fight Indians, I sure don't want to be ashamed of the men I've got to lead. All right, now, when I say *Attention*, stand up straight. *Attention!*"

He heard a couple of murmurs from dissenters, and received black looks from several who didn't like to take orders from any man, least of all that Abe Lincoln. But, somewhat urged by the fire in Jack Armstrong's eyes, most of the men pulled themselves together and, grinning self-consciously, stood at what they fancied was attention. Abraham looked down the uneven ranks and sighed.

It would take more than threats to make that bunch of loungers into a creditable company of soldiers, fit to tackle Indians.

"Well," he announced, not very hopefully. "I guess you can't do any better right now and neither can I. But I sure hope I can get all of us whipped into some sort of shape before we get up to Fort Armstrong, where there're some real soldiers and real officers, not to mention genuine Indians on the warpath. I do hope we aren't the laughingstock of this whole business!"

CHAPTER TWO

THE PEOPLE OF New Salem gathered along the broad and muddy main street to wave good-bye to their men, who had assembled on their horses. Even Lincoln had secured a mount by borrowing one from Squire Bowling Green.

"What if something happens to it?" Abraham had asked.

"Well, you can just write it off as my contribution to freedom and safety," answered Squire Green. "That horse can fight a better war than I ever could, heavy as I am!" Bowling Green weighed three hundred pounds and was troubled with shortness of breath.

Squire Green was on hand to wave farewell to the soldiers. So were the Rutledges and the Berrys, the Greenes and the Camrons, as well as little Doctor Allen, the Onstots and the Trents. Mentor Graham, the schoolmaster, was in town, quite by happen-chance, he declared. His few pupils, however, had not even shown up in school that day; they wanted to see the soldiers leave for the war. The eleven Camron girls and a quartet of Rutledge daughters clustered in a pretty bevy on the steps of the Rutledge tavern, to watch and wave. The young ladies were thrilled and excited by the nobility of the young men who were riding off to war.

"More fuss and excitement than a new rooster in the chicken house!" commented Royal Clary with some pleasure.

"Reminds me of the fellow who was about to start out for the War of 1812," put in Lincoln, "and wasn't hankering much to get into the fray, I guess. His sweetheart had lovingly embroidered for him a fancy bullet pouch—embroidered bullet pouches being so handy in the thick of battle! She had sewed on it the words *Victory or Death*. But the soldier turned a trifle pale on observing that lofty sentiment.

" 'Couldn't you make it a mite less final?' he suggested unhappily. Maybe *Victory or—or—Wounds?* That'd give me a little more leeway betwixt one and t'other!' "

Lincoln's listeners all laughed, but somewhat uneasily.

"Makes me think of all of us," he added with a wry grin. "All keyed up to go off and fight, but hoping it won't be quite as bad as we're afraid to think it will be. Makes us all figure we'd likely faint at the sight of blood, especially our own!"

The men grinned uncertainly at Abraham, not sure of what he was driving at and wishing they could be on their way with no more fuss and talk. It was uncomfortable standing about like this in the hill village above the Sangamon River, waiting for stragglers to show up, trying to make a good account of themselves, but feeling a little like fools with everyone looking on like that and spouting advice.

The little boys, meanwhile, terribly envious of what their elders were about to do and wishing they could go along and take a crack at an Indian, too, punched each other and rolled in the mud. They were somewhat absently scolded by their mothers or big sisters. Yanked by the ears to an upright position, the boys stood still briefly and uneasily to watch, in hideous envy, and then were at it again. Some tagged along behind the troop as it finally set off.

"Company, attention!" barked Captain Abraham Lincoln in commanding tones, which he had practiced down in Purkapile Hollow all the afternoon before, and which brooked no such insolent reply as he'd gotten that first day when he became captain.

"For-ward *march!*"

And they were off—well, not marching, but riding. As the column set out, Abraham Lincoln spied Denton Offutt, his employer, in a soiled shirt and velvet waistcoat which was somewhat the worse for the pork gravy he had lately consumed. Mr. Offutt, puffing a large cigar, was watching the parade in some amusement.

"Good-bye, Mr. Offutt," called Abraham as he rode past. "I'll be back as soon as I can. I do hope you'll make out all right with the store—this war sure can't last very long, so I'll be on hand to sell your seed-corn when the time comes."

"Sure, sure, Lincoln," soothed Denton Offutt, cherishing his cigar delicately between two grimy fingers in order to speak.

"I have my doubts as to whether I or my place of business will even be here when you return from the field of war. Anyway, that there seed-corn ain't first rate; rats got into it durin' the winter, and I reckon it won't sell well. I have big plans, though, for a project down in St. Louis, my boy. New Salem has proved too small for a profitable venture . . . but be that as it may, good-bye, son, and don't you run into no bloodthirsty redskins if you kin he'p it!"

Denton Offutt laughed loudly. Abraham smiled weakly and turned his attention to the company. Men and horses, with jingling harness and the creak of saddle leather, took to the rutted road toward Beardstown, forty miles away. Two days later they had arrived in camp.

High water in the Illinois River had put half the river-front shacks of Beardstown awash, but the higher country of the sand dunes was dry enough for a camp. Captain Lincoln and his company joined other captains and companies, all as raw, uneasy and untrained as his. They made him feel considerably better—or worse— he figured, thinking of the colossal amount of ignorance and headstrongness which lay encamped on the sandy, cactus-infested acres outside Beardstown.

On April 28, 1832, while the prairie larks twittered in the sand fields, Colonel John Hardin, Inspector General of Illinois, mustered in the untrained ranks of new recruits. He assigned Abraham Lincoln and his company to the Fourth Regiment.

Abraham found his job one of the toughest, if one of the greatest honor, he had ever known. To get any order or crispness out of that company of his, besides, was an endless ordeal, and he had so little time in which to do it. He was, also, impressed with his own lamentable ignorance of army procedure.

At Beardstown, where they camped for two days, he regularly drilled his men, up and down, back and forth, dodging cactus stickers and woodchuck burrows and early rattlesnakes. This exercise was intended as much to keep the soldiers out of mischief as to train them, and it helped him, besides, to remember the commands he had to use.

It was when he was marching his men twenty abreast across the hummocky sand fields that suddenly trouble loomed ahead. A fence . . . a gate opening into the next field . . . a gate only wide enough for no more than two persons to pass through at a time. In the press of the moment, he couldn't think of what order would get his men turned endwise, to march through in single file. As the company, advancing at a more or less smart clip through the loose sand and cactus plants, approached this bottleneck, he was desperate. There was only one thing to do and he did it.

He wheeled to face them.

"Company, halt! This company is dismissed for two minutes. At the end of that time, form ranks on the other side of the gate!"

Grinning, the men scattered, went through the gate, and reassembled the company. In considerable relief, Captain Lincoln went on with his drill.

But there was little time for training men for the real job which lay ahead. On April 30, the Fourth Regiment marched or rode out of Beardstown and was ferried across the Illinois River, to continue on the other shore, northwest. From the wet bottomlands, where hordes of disturbed redwinged blackbirds got up, shrilling, as the men rode the muddy trail bisecting the big swamp, they reached higher ground at last. They were on their way north to the Rock River and Black Hawk's country.

Supplies came by steamboat up the Mississippi to the mouth of the Rock River. The boat was unloading when the new militia from farther south, already sick of the monotony and weariness of war, straggled in to make camp beside the river, opposite Black Hawk's old village.

Abraham Lincoln was thankful they had arrived. He had had

a hard time keeping his unruly recruits from foraging for food and plunder at farms which they passed and from shooting off their muskets for the sheer joy of making a noise. Jack Armstrong, as his first lieutenant, had helped him enforce rules and keep a degree of order, but Lincoln felt as if he had been conducting a company of schoolboys on a spring outing, rather than a responsible troop of militia out to subdue the Indians.

Several days after their arrival, however, it was Captain Lincoln himself who was in disgrace.

It happened that a private in Captain Thomas McDow's company entered the officers' quarters one night. With the aid of a hatchet and four buckets, and willingly assisted by some of the Clary's Grove boys in Lincoln's company, the raiders succeeded in breaking open whiskey barrels and in making off with a considerable amount of strong drink.

At dawn, the bugles blew. The regiment was ordered out to march up the Rock River in pursuit of the Indians who were rumored to be lurking there. Action was evidently about to start, and Abraham Lincoln, in a way, was glad, though apprehensive as to how it would turn out.

A good many men in his company, however, couldn't stand up straight or didn't make it out of their blankets at all that drizzling spring morning.

Livid with rage, General Whiteside addressed himself to the mortified and furious Lincoln, who was tugging futilely at the delinquents who were still abed.

"*Captain Lincoln!*" barked the general wrathily, his bushy eyebrows scowling down over his sharp gray eyes. "Your leadership in this army is a pure disgrace! How do you expect your men to face an Indian attack in this sodden condition? How do you expect them to pursue wild, bloodthirsty savages and rid the land of their menace? I ask you! As a penalty for permitting this thievery and the drunken debauch in which these men have evidently indulged, you are to wear the wooden sword for two days! With it clapping you on the legs at every step, maybe you will be reminded of your duties as an officer! *Captain*—hah!—Lincoln, you are dismissed!"

Somehow, the regiment set out. Captain Lincoln was grim, tight of jaw, unhappy. The shameful wooden sword, the equivalent of a dunce's cap in school, ignominiously knocked at his knees until he mounted his horse, when it annoyed that animal excessively by striking its flank as it set forth.

As the revelers, bleary-eyed and sick, began to sober up, they realized something of what they had done. It had been all their fault that Lincoln was disgraced like that and looked so gloomy. He was having to pay up for their sins.

"He oughtn't to've been punished for what we done," muttered Travice Elmore, wishing his head didn't ache so and his horse didn't jounce so much as it walked.

"Naw, 'twasn't none of his fault what we done, and we got to make it up to him somehow or another," added Royal Potter.

"Well, what you reckon we can do?" asked Pleasant Armstrong sickly.

"We could act as much like good soldiers as we know how, which sure ain't much," put in Potter soberly. "We could try, anyways."

"Yeah, might be a good idea in more ways than one," Jack Armstrong commented acidly, from behind the speakers. "I'm warnin' you, boys," he went on darkly, "if you cause Lincoln any more trouble, you have me to answer to. And I can lick any one of you singlehanded, drunk *or* sober, and mop up the floor with you afterward, and I'll do it if you don't treat him better. You hear?"

"We hear," said the others solemnly.

After that, Captain Lincoln was considerably surprised at what a model company he had, barring a few slip-ups; how well they marched, how well they acted, how quickly and even cheerfully they took orders and assumed duties. He said nothing about it and neither did the men, but Jack Armstrong had a satisfied gleam in his eyes. They all knew they had to square things and this was the best way to do it.

But everyone, good or bad, wished action would begin. Here they were in the Indian country, near the evil Prophet's town, from which he and his people had vanished, and no one caught a glimpse of any Indian, much less had a chance to fire a shot at one. For want of anything more exciting to do, the soldiers burned the Prophet's village. Leaving the smouldering ruins, they continued up Rock River, while the rain came down, day after day, and drenched men and equipment.

And it was at this point of boredom that Major Stillman set forth to rout out Black Hawk and put a little action into this disappointing war.

CHAPTER THREE

AFTER STILLMAN'S DEFEAT, Governor Reynolds called for more volunteers. Instead of a somewhat aimless pursuit of Black Hawk's war band, the militia now tried desperately to catch up with the Indians, who were said to be traveling up the Rock River to the north. The militia followed that winding, beautiful stream as it curved between hills and past great rock outcroppings. Upon these and behind these, Indians could have lurked to pick off as many of the unsuspecting soldiers as they had wished.

But Black Hawk and his people were not there. Knowing the secret paths through the forests and over the prairies, they had no need of following the river route. Black Hawk's people were taking the short cuts, the quick trails, heading toward the Mississippi, while the white men were laboriously going the long way around, making every bend of the bending river. Morale was very low.

On a fine May morning, warm of sun and alive with the freshness of full-leafed spring, an old Potawatomi Indian limped into the camp. No one noticed his approach. Soldiers, squatting on their heels to cook their breakfasts over smoking little fires, were too much engrossed with the coming food to pay much attention to visitors.

One man, suddenly looking up, discovered the ragged old Indian standing irresolutely near the flagpole.

"Good-gosh-a-mighty!" the soldier yelped, getting up so suddenly from his stooping position that his sizzling chunk of bacon fell into the fire. "Look! An Injun! Get him, boys!"

"Injuns!" someone screeched unwisely. "Shoot him down before he gets us!"

The old man blanched. He fumbled, trembling, in his tattered clothing, hunting frantically for a grimy, folded piece of paper. Shaking, he stretched it forth, but no one paid any attention to what he held. Over the camp, guns were being hastily loaded. There was an ominous sound of hammers being cocked, when Captain Lincoln discovered the situation and loped on long legs to the side of the Indian.

He took the paper the man held out to him. The fear in the old fellow's eyes reminded Abraham of a deer beset by wolves on the ice.

The paper was a safe-conduct pass from General Lewis Cass.

"It's all right, men," Captain Lincoln reassured them. "You don't have to worry. General Cass vouches for him. This is old Wa-Pa-Qunt, the White Hare, on his way down to Fort Armstrong. Let him go."

"Not us!" spoke up one of the men belligerently, stepping forward. "We been huntin' Injuns three weeks and ain't seen none till now. He's a Injun, ain't he? Well, that's enough for me, ain't it for you, men? The only good Injun's a dead one, and I aim to make him mighty good in about two shakes. Stand out'n the way, Lincoln!"

Abraham Lincoln instead placed himself protectively in front of the cowering Potawatomi. The captain was furious, his face dark with anger, his big fists clenched. If there was anything that riled him, it was injustice to the weak.

"Get out of the way yourself, Hank Rhoads, before I knock you down where you stand! Haven't you got any sense of decency? This is an old man, weak and helpless; he needs our help, and you want to shoot him down just because he's an Indian! Put up that musket, I tell you, and that applies to the rest of you hotheads, or by jing, I'll do it for you in a way you won't like! Uncock them, and fast!"

"He's just foolin' you, Cap," one man assured Abraham, moving in a little closer, musket ready. "That paper don't mean nothin'. It's just a trick to find out our position and get through so we can be attacked from the rear. Oh, I know them redskins. Can't trust ary one of them!"

"I said put up your guns!" roared Lincoln, thoroughly out of patience. "This man goes through our lines without harm!"

"You're a coward, Lincoln," sneered Jacob Stolzfuss, with an ugly look, thrusting out his shaggy lower jaw. "Yellow clean through!"

"Just step over here a minute, will you, Jake?" said Abraham, deceptively calm. "That's it, over here. I didn't think I heard you clear, but I reckon I did, at that. Now," as the man stepped within reach of those long arms, "say it again!" he cried and knocked down the surprised Jacob.

"Any more of you boys who think I'm a coward can walk up now and we'll settle it," said Lincoln gently, dusting his hands on his breeches.

"That ain't no fair fight," objected Parmeneas Conway. "You got a longer reach, stand taller 'n' got more strength. You can't prove nothin' thataway."

"Can't I?" Abraham smiled, waiting.

No one seemed very eager to find out. Lincoln stood with the old Indian, who had grown more calm in the protective shadow of his champion's bulk and power.

"Well, that takes care of the matter, I reckon," concluded Lincoln cheerfully. "White Hare stays to breakfast, and then he goes, and nobody hurts, scares, insults or otherwise molests him. You hear?"

There was considerable muttering, but the guns were uncocked and put down.

"Only chance we get to take a good crack at a Injun and Lincoln won't let us," he heard muttered around.

"Oh, shut up!" snapped Jack Armstrong, tightening his own fists in full view. "What Lincoln says goes, and I'll back him up like I expect you to do. Now git! Eat breakfast and you'll feel better."

All of this, however, did not help morale in the camp nor among other battalions where the same trouble was rampant. The month's enlistment for which most of the men felt they had signed up was coming to an end, and although they were expected to reenlist for the duration of the war, few were inclined to do so.

"We want to go home!" spoke up Royal Clary one night after a long, futile day of mud-slogging and mosquitoes. "The food is rotten, the tents leak, our clothes are always damp and never dry out between one day's march and the next. Besides, our horses are ailin' and a lot have died, and the government ain't givin' us any replacements. We've had enough!"

"And we want to go now! This here rain is no good for marchin' or ridin'! My fields is goin' to need plowin' and plantin' right soon now, if it ever drains off, and I'm goin' home to do it!"

"So are we!" chorused half a dozen others. "This is a crazy kind of life, chasin' Injuns we never get a squint at, much less a shot!"

"You'll go home when you're mustered out proper!" snapped Abraham Lincoln, out of patience with the eternal grumbling he had been enduring. Secretly, he rather wished that he, too, might have a chance to go back to New Salem, where he would have a roof over his head, a bed at night and three good meals a day, as well as some dry, mended clothes and shoes.

"When General Whiteside gets here, you tell your troubles to him!"

But before the complaints of the volunteers could be attended to, Black Hawk struck again, and hard.

One night he held counsel with his war leaders and certain members of the Potawatomis and Winnebagoes, who agreed to help him in a mass attack upon the whites. The leaders sat in the counsel ring, their dark faces lit from below by the fire they circled, and nodded in aquiline agreement—all but short, broad-faced, honest Shabbona, a Potawatomi.

Shabbona had been a friend of the white people for a long time and he had been well treated by them. Must he, he wondered desperately, revert to the old ways, or would he be able to save his friends? Tumultuous and conflicting thoughts tumbled through

Shabbona's mind as he quietly got up and left the meeting. He believed he went undetected, but Black Hawk's keen eyes noted his absence, and with a gesture, he sent several of his Sac warriors to trail the Potawatomi. But Shabbona, stopping only to enlist the help of his son, Py-pes, had a head start.

The two Indians, on horses, set off to warn the scattered settlements. Hampered though the two were, with scarcely any knowledge of English, and constantly aware that, as Indians, they were likely to be shot first and questioned later, they nevertheless rode, like a pair of dark-skinned Paul Reveres, through the night. They galloped up to farmhouses, pounded on doors, somehow made the startled inhabitants understand that Black Hawk was coming . . . Black Hawk was coming . . . and the settlers, in terror, hurried to the newly built forts . . . and waited.

On Indian Creek, the Davis family felt that the danger was over-dramatized. There had been so many false alarms. They were tired of running whenever anyone cried, "Black Hawk!" They stayed, and nothing happened.

Meanwhile, several families who had fled to Ottawa, Illinois, for safety decided to come back to their homes. On their way, they gathered with the Davises over night. There were fifteen people in this cabin, and by their very numbers they felt safe. But Shabbona's son, passing in the vicinity, discovered a large number of Black Hawk's men camping inconspicuously nearby, ready for an assault when the time was right and the signal given. The young Indian hastened to the Davis cabin to urge the people to go to Ottawa for their lives, but the men felt they could hold off an attack, should one come, which they doubted. Besides, they hated to go off and leave the farm and livestock to the mercy of Indian or thief. They stayed.

But the Sacs and Foxes were closing in. They were slipping through the woods, sliding from tree to tree, circling the cabin in the oak clearing. Suddenly, a dog at the Davises' began a frantic barking, which changed to an agonized howl as a tomahawk, flung at its head, split its skull.

23

Mrs. Davis, looking out, screamed:

"They've come! Indians! They're here!"

It was too late then to do anything. The young children were picked up by the feet and slammed against stumps. Women and men were slaughtered and scalped. Thirteen people died in the massacre.

Young Rachael Hall, who was fifteen, and her pretty sister, Sylvia, seventeen, in horror watched their parents and family slain. They, however, were not harmed, but were taken as captives by the Indians who hustled them along through the woods when the slaughter was over. Long afterward, when they were rescued, it was they who told all the terrible details of the Indian Creek massacre.

If Stillman's defeat had unnerved the already pretty badly demoralized troops, the news from Indian Creek was the final straw. The men definitely did not want any part of such a dangerous business. They wanted to go home. Major Buckmaster was downright disgusted with the complaining. He had been finding it in all the regiments sent to protect the settlers.

"By the Lord Harry!" he fumed. "You enlisted for thirty days, but you are expected to re-enlist for the duration of this war! You think you can cut and run just because war is too strong for your weak stomachs! Yes, I'll muster you out, you flabby backsliders, and I'd like to do it at the end of a bayonet, you lazy, shameless excuses for soldiers!" Buckmaster ranted.

"The whole of northern Illinois and Michigan Territory could be overrun with Indians and the settlers killed in their beds, and all you'd do would be to whine to go home! Well, *go* home, and I hope you sleep well at night, thinking back on what you've done for your country. Think of the bloody scalps of women and children. I hope the thoughts give you pleasant dreams!"

Before the men were allowed to go, however, the officers grimly searched them for plunder taken from Indian towns along the way. At Paw Paw village, they had found scalps taken from Stillman's men. Some of the soldiers had joyfully confiscated this loot, hiding the grim trophies in their packsacks. The latter however, were searched and the men were relieved of all their loot before being permitted to depart. Governor Reynolds himself, on the field, taking chances and hardships with the rest, in disgust and grief watched a large portion of his Illinois militia go righteously homeward.

Abraham Lincoln and a good many of the New Salem men stayed. Abraham, however, was now devoid of a company to command. He re-enlisted as a private under Captain Elijah Iles. Here he was thrown into the companionship of tall, handsome, dashing John Todd Stuart, a rising young lawyer of Springfield, Illinois, who somehow took an immediate fancy to the roughly dressed, honest-eyed fellow from New Salem. Abraham could hardly see why the aristocratic John Stuart would enjoy his company. Stuart came of a wealthy Kentucky family and was college-educated, but that didn't seem to prevent his affection for the self-taught Lincoln, who also came from Kentucky, though there all similarity of background ended abruptly. Abraham shrugged. If it didn't matter to Stuart, it surely didn't matter to Lincoln.

Lincoln and Stuart set off with a newly enlivened army in a continued aimless pursuit of the Indians. The militia traveled north to the lead mines country at Galena, where fear of an attack was rampant after the Indian Creek tragedy. On their return, still not finding the enemy, the troops were in time to clean up after the Kellogg's Creek massacre.

Once again, Abraham Lincoln had to help bury men who had been scalped and mutilated by the Indians, while the turkey buzzards circled, waiting, or came down boldly to the dead horses.

Now that the army was in earnest about his capture, Black Hawk changed his apparently pointless striking and running and headed northwest. At once, General Atkinson ordered troops to abandon the futile chase and hurry directly up the Mississippi, to head off Black Hawk before he should cross the river and escape.

Abraham, his shoes pretty badly worn out, was up at Lake

Koshkonong, in Wisconsin. It was early in July and he had been chasing Indians and not seeing any live ones ever since the end of April.

With the pursuit closing in, although the whole disturbance was not to end until the bloody Battle of Bad Ax, a month later, General Atkinson suddenly decided to muster out part of the scattered army. Food and supplies were scarce, and it was impossible to maintain so large a force without better support and more money. Consequently, to his secret delight, Abraham Lincoln and the men in his company were honorably mustered out.

He woke, the morning after, with a grand feeling of freedom in his heart. He was going home, home to New Salem, home to the people he had grown to love.

Abraham scrambled out of his tent and stretched in the crisp morning air. He went over to the shore of shining Lake Koshkonong, where the yellow-headed blackbirds clattered. He squatted on his heels and doused the cold, clear water on his face. Back in his tent, he looked about for his shoes. They were tattered and uncomfortable, but at least they still somewhat protected his feet. There was a long way to go ahead of him, almost three hundred miles south to New Salem.

The shoes, however, seemed to be missing. He searched, puzzled. They were too battered for anyone else to want them. Then he discovered the vanished footgear at last, between the paws of a slumbering camp dog. The animal had pretty thoroughly completed their demolition by chewing and worrying them. Sadly, Abraham did not even try to retrieve them. From what he could see in their final ruin, they would do little to protect his feet any more. Well, at least he would be able to ride home.

But his lean and bony horse, borrowed from Squire Green of New Salem, seemed to be missing too. So were some of the other horses. Evidently certain men, departing expediently in the night, had taken with them whatever they needed, well before anyone was awake to detect the theft.

The other men were up now, stretching, groaning at having to

LINCOLN HIMSELF WAS WORRIED. THINGS WERE TOO QUIET. . . . ACTION . . . WOULD
CERTAINLY BE BETTER THAN THIS TERRIBLE WAITING.

"I DIDN'T THINK I HEARD YOU CLEAR, BUT I RECKON I DID. . . . NOW," AS THE MAN
STEPPED WITHIN REACH OF HIS LONG ARMS, "SAY IT AGAIN!"

face another day, but cheered by the prospect of home.

"Have you seen my horse, Jerry?" Abraham asked a friend, who was vigorously scratching himself through his dirty shirt.

"Horse? No, why would I see your horse—oh, you mean, it's missin'? Heck, no, I ain't seen your horse, I been asleep, though how ary man kin sleep on ground as hard as that, with all them rocks in it, and all them mosquitoes, ants and ticks crawlin' and bitin', I can't see. Your horse gone?"

"Seems like," said Abe soberly.

"What's the trouble, Lincoln?" asked John Stuart, already impeccably shaved and dressed, wearing shoes which still had good soles, trousers which came neatly down to where they were supposed to come and a clean shirt. But Stuart was quality, even if he did hail from Springfield. Knowing John Stuart had been a bright light in an otherwise pretty dreary campaign, Abraham Lincoln felt. Stuart had promised to do something for him if he ever wanted to go into the practice of law.

Abraham looked up from where he was trying to tie some pieces of canvas around his big, bare, cold feet; his socks were long since worn out. He had stony ground and a long trip ahead.

"Nothing much, Stuart," he said cheerfully, though he did not feel so gay. "My horse has gone on a vacation and that delightful dog there has made a meal of what was left of my shoes. Not that he got much nourishment from them, I'm sure, since I'd already walked holes in the soles and uppers, but I might have made out with them a mile or two."

"Why, Lincoln, I'm sorry about that!" Stuart was genuinely distressed. "I wish I had a pair you could use, but my feet, well, you can see that my shoes would scarcely fit you . . . I can let you have money, though."

"No place to buy shoes, Stuart, if I had the cash to lay down. No, don't worry. I've walked before and walk I shall again. See you in Springfield—some day!"

"I'll walk with you, Lincoln, if you want company," put in George Harrison ruefully. "Seems as if my horse has gone off, too, so if you think I can keep up, I'll go a way with you."

"Hold on a minute," spoke up Stuart. "If we all start out together, you men without horses can ride a while and some of the others can walk. We'll take turns. Do us good, and that way you won't have to walk all that distance!"

"Well, say, Stuart, that's handsome of you!" Lincoln smiled at his friend and extended his hand. "We'll do that, if you all don't object. At least until we get down to the Illinois River. Once there, we can take to the water and ride the rest of the way by boat."

Consequently, swapping rides, the two made it to Peru on the Illinois. The horsemen waved their farewells, while Harrison and Lincoln raked up enough cash money between them to buy a heavy old cottonwood-log canoe, in which they proposed to go downstream.

Paddling, however, was a tedious business. In July, the river was low, green and leisurely, in no hurry to go anywhere. To save time and perhaps get a little farther, the pair remained somewhat uncomfortably in the canoe all night and let their craft drift, but by next morning they were often still within sight of some point which they remembered having passed the day before. Poling, paddling, they made it a little faster, enough to stir up the water a bit, anyway.

One day about noon, they caught up with a big lumber raft. It was drifting slowly with what current there seemed to be in the crawling, torpid, green river, which was like slow soup on the hot July day. Beds of lotuses in the shallows steamed in the heat, the big yellow flowers open wide, some dropping their heavy petals, their fragrance rising almost sickeningly in the humid heat. Great blue herons, squawking, got up from the mud flats and flapped heavily away as the two craft neared.

The crew on the raft hailed the pair in the canoe.

"Hi! Where you bound?"

"Oh, Havana, maybe, or Beardstown. Where *you* bound?"

"St. Louis, if we ever get there on a river like this. Stay in one place for days, likely, if we didn't shove a little. You et dinner yet?" the raftsman added. People always seemed to think of food when they took a good look at Abraham Lincoln's lank length, lean face and hungry countenance.

"No, we sure haven't," said Harrison briefly, trying not to seem too eager. A fragrant smoke was rising from a sand box on the raft. Dinner was obviously in the air.

"Neither have we, but we're about to. Got plenty. Tie on and come aboard and eat with us."

It took no time at all for the pair to tether the canoe to a cleat and scramble on to the broad expanse of the lumber raft, which had come down from the forests of the upper Illinois. The food was wonderful to the two men who had subsisted on their own cooking of meager camp fare for more than two months. Hot, crisp cornbread with butter melting into it, boiled sweet corn, fried catfish sizzling in bacon fat, coffee and raw onions strong enough to make you reel. It was a feast to put new heart into the two. Food could make all the difference between melancholy and hope, between despair and ambition. Right now, Lincoln felt he could use a little hope and ambition. He was going back to New Salem, to no job and no visible prospects.

He wiped his mouth as he finished his fourth ear of corn and pitched the cob into the river.

"That was mighty tasty!" he exclaimed. "I reckon the only time I ever turned against food, though," he went on, "was the day I was invited to take supper over at the Elmores', near New Salem. They were having side meat and sauerkraut, which I relish tolerably well, but when I forked into it and dredged up a long piece of blue yarn, I got kind of confused. I didn't know whether I ought to swallow it politely or dispose of the thing as inconspicuously as possible, so as not to hurt the cook's feelings. But Mrs. Elmore spied it, and she just laughed. Nothing ever bothers Jemima Elmore!"

" 'Oh, I see you've found a piece of string in your dinner, Abe,' she tittered. She's a great one to titter. 'Now don't you fret a mite. That's just a strand of Clara's stockin' that she had on when we made kraut. Must of come unraveled-like whilst Clara was trampin' the cabbage into the churn we keep it in!'

"Yes, I kind of lost my appetite after that, just casting my mind back a little at big, fat, greasy Clara and wondering when those stockings of hers had been washed last—or Clara, for that matter!"

With stories and with reminiscences of the war, the pair came with the raft to Havana. Once more they got into the canoe and paddled to a sandy shore baking in the sun. A swarm of blood-thirsty mosquitoes met them as they landed. A big snapping turtle, almost as large as a washtub, opened its whitish mouth and hissed angrily and nastily at them as the creature waddled awkwardly out of the way and plunged into the water. It had been champing on a dead carp whose mangled remains steamed fetidly in the sunshine. Close by lay a polished Indian ax. George Harrison nudged it with his toe.

"Indians been here, seems like," he commented.

"I'd just as soon forget the Indians for a while," said Abraham firmly. The vision of scalped men still stayed with him, especially at night.

Although Abraham Lincoln did not exactly return a hero, he felt good to be back. It was a trifle embarrassing, however, to arrive as he did, a lone private with no shoes, only some old moccasins one of the raftsmen had given him, when he had nobly ridden off as a well-shod captain at the head of a troop of men only two months before. Nearly all of those who had enlisted in April were back ahead of him. A good many thought Lincoln had been killed; hadn't seen him or heard any word of him in weeks.

"Did you have a big time fightin' them Injuns, Abe?" quavered old Enos Short, who had fought in the Revolution. His palsied hands clung to his cane.

"Well, now, Mr. Short," said Abraham solemnly, as he leaned against the shady side of Sam Hill's store. "I *could* say I fought and bled for my country, and, after all, what more can any soldier say? I wasn't at Stillman's defeat, but I must admit I saw the place all too soon afterward! I reckon I didn't break my sword in combat, because I hadn't one to break, and wasn't in any combat, either, but I recall I bent a musket pretty badly on one occasion by dropping it on the rocks. I may not have had the honor of leading a charge on old Black Hawk, but I sure headed a good many fierce and hungry assaults upon the wild onions!"

"Did you see ary Injuns, Abe?" asked Mr. Short wistfully, only half hearing, remembering the days when there was an Indian hiding behind almost any bush you could mention, and you had to watch out for them day and night.

"Well, no, I'm mighty glad to say I didn't see any live, fighting Indians, Mr. Short, only one very old and scared one," he went on with a smile twinkling in his eyes. "But I reckon I had a good many bloody encounters with the mosquitoes, and though I'll admit I never fainted from loss of blood, there were times there when I was mighty hungry . . . as I am now. Mrs. Graham, ma'am," he turned to address that lady, who had come to the store, "do you suppose there might be an extra plate at your table tonight?"

Sarah Graham's cornflower eyes snapped beneath level black brows. She could quell any man with those eyes and with a brisk application of her acid tongue, but her words were surprisingly gentle, considering her disposition.

"Well, Mr. Lincoln, I was just about to suggest it myself. It'll be a fine honor for us to have you come to supper, and you might as well stay all night, too. Haven't had a chance to hear all your news, and Mentor'll be glad of a chance to gab with you till all hours. Reckon that'll keep me awake, but mayhap I'll just stay up to listen, too. Almira and Minerva have missed you, little though they are. They keep pesterin' me—'when's Mr. Lincoln comin' back, Mammy?' They do relish the stories you tell them and the little knickknacks you bring."

Abraham smiled warmly at the tall, thin woman in her neatly handmade gown and her broadly scooped, fashionable bonnet with the pale blue flowers perched high on the brim, and long ribbons tied under her chin. Poor though the Grahams often were, Sarah always dressed well.

"Thank you, ma'am, I'll be there and gladly. Haven't had any cooking that could touch yours since I left home. Home! That's a downright heartening word, isn't it? It's good to be back. You tell the little girls I'll be there soon, and I have some little oddments for them!"

31

CHAPTER FOUR

Ever since that July day a year earlier, when Abraham Lincoln had come hopefully down the Sangamon River to take a job at New Salem, Illinois, his roots had been set in the earth of that hilltop. He was twenty-two and on his own at last. He had piloted Denton Offutt's loaded flatboat of produce down to New Orleans earlier that year, had contrived to by-pass danger and the menaces of three rivers, the Sangamon, the Illinois and the Mississippi, to deliver his cargo. The big boat had caught on the dam at New Salem when the water had begun to drop, and the great craft, loaded with pork and hogs, corn and whiskey, could not clear the log-pilings of the dam. The flatboat had had to be unloaded and finally floated off, but not before boat and crew had spent almost twenty-four hours in the New Salem neighborhood and had impressed their varied personalities upon its people.

Offutt, rotund, talkative and a heavy drinker, in particular had been much pleased with New Salem's favorable situation on the top of a high, wooded hill, above the curving Sangamon River. This place, a shopping and business point for a wide surrounding area, was just beginning to attract settlers. It held promise of rapid and permanent growth. To profit by this, Denton Offutt had vowed to return and set up a business on the hill.

New Salem had come into existence in 1829, when John Camron, a Cumberland Presbyterian minister, and his uncle, James Rutledge, up from South Carolina by way of Kentucky, built a combination sawmill and grist mill on the river below the then uninhabited hill. People who came to have their corn ground into meal or their logs sawed into rough planks for floors of cabins which were springing up in Illinois clearings, often hailed from so far away that they could not get back home that night. This was especially true when there was a crowd, and the miller had to take his customers by turns. In the busy season, when the mill hummed and the millstones ground and champed at the hard yellow corn, and the saw grated like a huge locust buzzing stridently into the air, men camped on the hillside. Their horses were tethered nearby, and boys went swimming or fishing while they waited.

There was a great need for a place of lodging, a place, as well, to buy food and drink. Consequently, James Rutledge and his sons enlarged the log house on the hilltop, built earlier just for the big Rutledge family, and made it available as the Rutledge Tavern.

Some of the transient guests were much attracted by the situation of the town.

"It's safe from floods," they said, "and high enough above the bottoms to be clear of bad air."

"The woods're full of good timber; lots of maple and oak and some of the biggest walnut I've ever laid eyes on."

"Good open country to the west, too. If they just get some decent roads laid, or else open up that river for steamboats, this place'd be perfect for a town."

People began moving here and building log houses. James Rutledge and John Camron, both deeply religious men, named their village New Salem for its biblical significance; *Salem* was the ancient name of Jerusalem. The two hoped that the new site might become a New Jerusalem of godly living in the west.

Rutledge had the area surveyed and the town platted; the lots were numbered and many soon were sold. Houses were arranged along a broad main street, which extended from the edge of the bluff to the west. Bluff and road formed an L-shape where the hill angled, like a boomerang, just above the river. At this point, the road descended to the river itself, to the mill and to the roads to Havana, northward, and to Springfield, southeastward.

It was on this eminence, just before the road dipped, that William Clary, in order to supply the need for strong drink which pioneer men felt and usually demanded, opened a grocery, which was just another name for a grog shop. He carried the usual homemade whiskey, distilled from the surplus corn crop each year; he also sold the more expensive and tasty rye whiskey, called Old Monongahela, as well as spirits of sugar cane, labeled *tafia*, and sometimes a rare keg of rum, up from the West Indies via New Orleans and the Mississippi.

It was close to this place of business that Denton Offutt planned to build his store and fill it with merchandise, foods and seed-corn from St. Louis. He would be in competition not so much with William Clary, who sold mostly liquid refreshment and attracted the toughs of the neighborhood, but with Samuel Hill and John McNeil, already the richest men in town, who had the best stocked store. Besides, there was Reuben Radford's store near Hill's, and Rowan Herndon's store, in partnership with William Berry, across the street.

On a summer day in 1831, a steamboat up from New Orleans discharged three men at the St. Louis landing. One of the three was Denton Offutt, who remained in that busy city to arrange for goods for his new store. The others, Abraham Lincoln and Jack Johnston, his young stepbrother, were ferried across the river to the Illinois shore, from which point they set off to walk to what was now home—the place where Thomas Lincoln and his family had moved in Coles County.

The Winter of the Deep Snow had been too much for Tom Lincoln. If Illinois winters were all like that, he figured, they weren't for him, no matter if the land was rich enough to grow cornstalks like oak trees. He'd take the south. But he'd had enough of southern Indiana, too. Fourteen years of fighting the yellow clay of an Indiana hilltop and of watching his topsoil wash down Pigeon Creek after every rain, had taken a lot out of Tom Lincoln. He was an old man now—he felt old, which was worse than having had fifty-three birthdays—and he wanted to take it easy.

On the advice of folk who claimed they knew what they were talking about, the Lincolns packed up their few belongings from the cabin they had built, with John Hanks' help, on the crest above the Sangamon River, west of Decatur. They migrated south to Coles County, Illinois, to more yellow clay and to fields which the orange broom sedge rapidly reclaimed if a farmer was not too diligent with the plow and harrow.

There Tom Lincoln put up another cabin. It was very much like all the rest he had built. Sarah Lincoln, patiently and with resignation, set up housekeeping. She was thankful that she at least had a plank floor and glass panes in her windows, though there was not much else in the two-room cabin except the furniture which she had brought to her marriage with Tom Lincoln in 1819. When the boys came back from their flatboat trip, they would have a longer way to go, and that on foot, unless they rode with someone going to Vincennes or New Harmony.

But Abe Lincoln and fair-haired, lazy Jack Johnston, following the National Road and then turning north, walked the whole way across the state, from St. Louis to Tom Lincoln's house.

They had to ask the direction several times, for although they knew the general location, they were not certain just where it was that their father had settled.

They found him sitting and dozing in the shade on the north side of the cabin. Sarah, at the sound of voices, hastily came to the door, wiping her work-roughened hands on her apron. She tried to gather both boys into one great, loving embrace. Abe picked his stepmother off the ground and held her out to look at for a moment, then kissed her with a vigor which warmed her through and through and set her cap awry.

"H'lo, Maw," said Jack briefly, going into the cabin. "Got somethin' to eat? I'm hungry!"

"Tell us about your trip, Abe," said Sarah, casting a sad glance toward her unresponsive son. "We've thought of you so often, and there were times, I declare, I had the most awful feelin' I'd never see you again, either one! Were you ever in danger; did aught happen to harm you?"

35

Abraham looked at his stepmother. He was recollecting certain moments when he and the crew of the flatboat had indeed been in considerable difficulty on that journey down three rivers south to the rambunctious city of New Orleans. He remembered how he had rescued Jack from the hang-out of river pirates, and of several other incidents . . .

"Well, yes, Mother," he answered slowly, "there were a couple of times I had my doubts we'd make it, but we did. We sure did—and here we are to prove it!"

"Yes, Son," said Sarah Lincoln softly. "I prayed and prayed, especially when I had a feeling—well, I knew that something was wrong, and I just prayed harder and the Lord listened, and here you are, praise be! Now come in, supper's nigh ready, and I know you're both hungry as bears. We can talk whilst we eat."

"Not me," grunted Tom Lincoln, heaving himself out of the splint chair. Groaning with a crick in his back, he carried his chair to the table. "When I'm eatin', I don't want no jawin'. Can't eat and talk, too, both at once, and get any good out of ary one. We'll eat first, then hear what them rascals has to say, if they's anythin' worth listenin' to, which I have my doubts of."

Abraham didn't stay long with his folks. It no longer felt much like home. Dennis Hanks and his family were living by themselves at last, and so were Levi and Matilda Hall and their young ones. There was plenty of room in the Lincoln cabin now. But Abraham Lincoln had that widened horizon, that broader view, which came from extensive travel, from seeing how other people lived and thought and did. Home seemed narrower and more cramped, his father more intolerable and intolerant than he ever had been before, which was saying a good deal. Abe felt that he himself had simply cracked out of his shell like a young bird and could never climb back in. The world was before him, and the broom sedge uplands of Coles County, Illinois, were only a small and uninspiring part of it, already seen and now ready to be discarded.

"I got me a job of work over to New Salem," Abraham announced one sultry day. "I promised to show up there by the end of July," he added, waiting to see the reaction. There was little.

Tom grunted. "Well, what's keepin' you, then? You're a man growed, and if you're ever a-goin' to make ary thing of yourself, you better get at it afore you're an old man like me and good for nothin'! When I was your age, I already owned property and horses.

"I'd have thought, though," Tom Lincoln went on in complaining tones, "that you'd-a got work closter to home, but that's like the young fellers nowadays. No thought of their parents that've give all to raise 'em up. No gratitude left these days."

"Oh, now, Tom," put in Sarah placatively, laying a hand on his sleeve. "You've done the best you could, and Abraham's grateful, I know he is. But he's got to get out in the world and make a livin' at what he finds is best for him. There's naught around here. Abe's got to take his chance where he gets it, and this New Salem, I hear tell, has a big future. You go, Son," she added lovingly, but wistfully, "though land knows I'll miss you like as if I'd lost my right arm or somethin'!"

"I'll try to come back often, Mother," he told her, seeing how worn her face was, how tired she looked, though her eyes were blue as ever and as full of life and love. "And as soon as I possibly can, I'll send you some money. As long as I live, you'll never want, if I can help it!"

"It won't matter about the money, Son," said Sarah quietly, in a low voice, looking up at him and taking his hands in hers, tightly, "just so's you come back sometimes and let me look at you."

"I promise," said Abe Lincoln, smiling down at her.

It was almost like coming home to reach New Salem again. There was considerable excitement in the village, but not about the newcomer. He arrived inconspicuously and found a place to board at John Camron's house, since the tavern itself was full. There were eleven girls at the Camrons', but not one of them seemed very much impressed with the tall young man with his sun-browned skin, hands thrusting too far out of his sleeves and pants legs not meeting his moccasins. He felt they liked him; most people did, he had discovered, but they laughed a little at him, too. He was just as glad they let him alone; girls somehow made him uneasy and were alarming when they paid too much attention to him. Not that he had had much chance for that, he admitted ruefully to himself in his loft bed, listening to the laughter of all those girls downstairs and wondering if it was he that so amused them. Might be, he admitted. But then, he guessed maybe it was better to amuse people than make them angry. Somehow the laughter gave him a lonely feeling, though.

The excitement in the village was over the annual election. It was coming up in a few days, on August 1, 1831. Abraham was immediately gathered up in the talk and argument about the values of the candidates, which flowed back and forth. He registered his name and on the big day he voted in John Camron's house. It was the first time in his life that Abraham had cast a vote, and the act made him feel thoroughly grown up at last, a man among men. He confidently voted for Edward Coles for congressman and for Bowling Green of New Salem for magistrate, and for Jack Armstrong and Henry Sinco for constables. He had only casually met several of the candidates, but voted anyway.

He hung around the polls early and stayed late. He was interested and spoke intelligently; he spiced the day with humorous stories. Mentor Graham, the dour-faced, red-haired schoolmaster who was clerk, finally asked him to help out.

"Can you write, sir?" he asked the tall youth, not having much hope of an affirmative reply from one as rough-looking and crude as this one.

"Well, yes, sir, I guess I can, somewhat," Abe admitted.

He demonstrated his penmanship, which was good and clear and readable, quite unlike a great deal of handwriting the schoolmaster had seen. The latter was visibly impressed.

"Where did you learn such excellent penmanship, Mr. Lincoln?"

"Well, I—I guess it just came naturally, as you might say," Abraham stumbled over his answer, hating to admit his meager educa-

38

tional background, but realizing he might as well and get it over with early in the game. "I've had only about a year or so of schooling in all. I went by littles, whenever there was a teacher in the neighborhood and money to pay him. But I always practiced hard on handwriting and spelling and such like, so I guess it'll pass."

"I should say it will! You sit here and record the names and votes for me while I go home and see how my wife is doing. She was ailing this morning, and I hated leaving."

Mentor Graham was not absent for very long, but Abraham Lincoln meanwhile had taken over the job of clerk with considerable relish and a fine flourish of the goosequill pen which elicited much admiration from the loungers at the polls. Abraham wondered briefly why John McNeil, partner over at Sam Hill's store, a very rich and influential young man who was engaged to Ann, one of the Rutledge girls, neither registered nor voted. Lincoln kept his questions to himself. He liked to talk, but he could also be as closemouthed as if he had eaten a green persimmon. It didn't behoove a newcomer to pry, but it did look funny, somehow. All the other men over twenty-one in New Salem and round about had registered and had come in proudly to cast their votes. But not John McNeil.

CHAPTER FIVE

As usual, Denton Offutt was behind schedule. He had told Abraham Lincoln to be at New Salem promptly by the first day of August, so that he could start clerking in his store. Not only did August first come and go without any sign of Mr. Offutt on the horizon, but there were no goods for the store. As a matter of fact, there was no store, either. That was the way it had been when he had hired Abe to pilot a flatboat down the rivers, and the young pilot had found that he had to build a boat before he could be a riverman!

When Denton Offutt and his ox-carts of merchandise finally arrived on the bluff, the goods had to be stored while Abe and young William Green squared off some logs and built a structure very much like William Clary's grocery store nearby. Clary sourly eyed the proceeding.

"Might at least have left me some elbowroom," he grumbled to the portly Denton Offutt, who was strutting about, his coat off in the heat, his untidy white ruffled shirt damp with perspiration and his suspenders running off purple on it, "and not've crowded in on me like this! You got the whole of Illinois to build a store in; why put it on *top* of me, I'd like to know?"

Denton Offutt beamed. "Well, now, sir," he stated pompously. "I figured this was a right favorable spot, as you might say. It's just up the hill from the mill and river and all, not to mention handy to the Springfield road and the Athens and Sangamo Town trade. With just your grocery here sellin' drinks, folk'll think it's not much use to climb all the way up and maybe not find what else they may fancy to buy and need mighty bad. But with two places, why, what they don't locate in one, they'll find in t'other, without the bother of traipsin' clear up the road to the other stores. Ain't that so, sir?"

William Clary didn't agree with this long-winded explanation.

"I don't favor it none," was all he would say. He stalked back into the dark grocery, where the aroma of whiskey and hard cider and persimmon beer was acrid on the air.

Jack Armstrong, hunched over the counter, a brooding look on his face, was silently drinking Old Monongahela. Armstrong was from Clary's Grove, west of town. He gave the impression of size, though he was not a tall man. Armstrong had broad, powerful shoulders; he was massive and very strong, a leader of the Clary's Grove boys.

"Mad, ain't you?" he remarked noncommittally.

"Enough to make a body think of clearin' out, I declare it is!" exclaimed William Clary fiercely, slamming his big, hairy hand down hard on the counter, while the whang of mallets on pegs and the crunch of log on log came through the open door. Flies buzzed dizzily around the bung of a whiskey barrel.

"Give that Offutt enough rope, he'll shore hang himself," consoled Armstrong. "I've seen the like of him before. You wait. *He* won't last. And as for that limber-legged grasshopper of a helper of his—though you can't hardly call him a helper, seein' he's doin' all the work, with Slicky Bill easin' off on the lighter end of things —well, we'll take care of him. Old Offutt's already braggin' his fool head off about how strong that Lincoln is, and how smart."

"Yeah, I know," agreed Clary acidly. "I heard him. Reckon folk all the way to Sandridge heard him, way he rants."

"Well, me and my buddies'll just take care of that Lincoln, and *he* won't stay to bother long!"

The store built and stocked, Abraham Lincoln had a job he liked. Presiding behind a counter, when there were customers handy, was much to his liking. Unhappily, there were not many of these.

During the slack periods, however, he could always improve the time by reading. It embarrassed him to hear Mr. Offutt brag about his, Lincoln's personal prowess.

"I tell you, my friends, this here Lincoln's the smartest feller you ever seen. That boy sure wasn't behind the door when they rattled the shucks! Besides, he's the strongest feller in all of Illinois —in the Middle West, I might even say and not exaggerate a mite," stout Mr. Offutt would spout grandly. "Bring on your champions of New Salem and round about, and my man'll lick every one of 'em, quicker'n a catfish kin skin a minner!"

"Oh, now, Mr. Offutt," Abe would protest in the middle of weighing out sugar or cutting off a twist of dog-leg.

"I'm right, I'm right," Denton Offutt would insist, downing another deep swig of Old Monongahela or applejack, whichever was handiest. "Bring 'em on, we'll take on all comers!"

"*We'll* take 'em on," fumed Abe, burning at the way the little man was rapidly courting trouble. "Oh, yes, *we'll* fight all comers, but who'll be the one that gets the knocks?"

"You got to watch out for that bunch of Clary's Grove boys," warned Judge Bowling Green. "Look what they did to old Jem Jordan last week. He was dead drunk, and they nailed him up in a barrel and rolled him down the hill, almost to the river. It's a pure wonder Jem lived through it, the barrel smashing against a tree and all, but maybe he was so drunk he didn't know what was happening. Anyway, you got to watch out for that gang, Lincoln. They're dangerous as a bunch of rattlesnakes on a hot day. Don't you go out of your way to make them mad. They think up enough deviltry without provoking them to more!"

One warm September day, when the hitching rack beside Clary's store was lined with horses stamping dust and switching their tails at flies, Jack Armstrong and some of his friends and relations from Clary's Grove (which amounted to the same thing because nearly everyone out there was kin to everyone else) got together in the matter.

"I've had all I can stand of that little fightin' cock of an Offutt.

Let's take on his baby and lay him out once and for all, and then maybe we can have some peace. I'm sick and tired of hearin' nothin' but how wonderful this feller Lincoln is. Come on!"

The Clary's Grove boys, few of whom were much less than six feet tall, men who were broad in the shoulders, narrow of hip, dark bearded and keen-eyed, guns handy and fists mighty, stalked out of Clary's grocery and across the dust to Offutt's store.

"You, Lincoln," spoke up brawny Jack Armstrong, shortest in stature of the group, lounging with a deceptive casualness in the doorway. Abraham, squinting at the light, looked at him.

"Sure, what you want, Jack?"

"I want you, Lincoln," said Jack Armstrong levelly, scowling at Abe's amiable face. "I'm mortal tired hearin' how all-fired strong you are. I'll concede maybe you're smarter'n me at books, but I aim to prove I'm stronger and always will be. Come out and fight."

"I'm working," said Abraham, but he got up from the puncheon stool, just the same.

"Yeah, looks like," sneered Armstrong. "Sittin' down with your nose into a book the whole endurin' time. It's plain to see you ain't got many customers. Well, when you think you ain't *too* busy nor *too* afeared, come out and I'll take you on, no holds barred!"

In a fury, Abraham put down his book. The pages, left alone, slowly flipped over and over until his place was quite lost. He hitched up his pants around his lean hips, rubbed his hands on the seat of his worn jeans and stalked out into the glare of the September afternoon.

At wind of a fight, a crowd was already gathering. It was largely composed of the rough, tough and mighty Clary's Grove boys, their bearded jaws working slowly around and around on cuds of tobacco, their eyes scornful, cold and watchful.

"I bet you ten dollars my man can beat yours," declared William Clary to Denton Offutt, who was delighted at the prospect of a fight—so long as he himself was not in it.

"Taken!" cried Offutt, and put down a ten-dollar gold piece beside Clary's sum. Ten dollars was a lot of money. The men eyed it with some respect and awe. A number of lesser bets were laid down, involving small coins, whiskey, knives and such. One man wagered his horse that Jack Armstrong would win hands down.

Young Slicky Bill Greene, his round face flushed with excitement, jiggled from one foot to the other, scared yet eager for the fight to start. He had been hired by Offutt to tell Lincoln whose credit was good and who couldn't be trusted to owe money. He admired and liked Abe Lincoln. In his own mind, he knew that Abe could lick anyone, no matter how strong, even the invincible Jack Armstrong. He had never actually seen Lincoln lick anybody, and he had only Denton Offutt's bragging to prove it—that, and Abe's own powerful arms and back, his hard muscles toughened by years of ax-swinging and hard work, and by his own calm sense of power. They were excellent convincers. Nevertheless, Billy Greene was as nervous as a wasp in locust time.

Stripped to the waist, their chest muscles and arms taut, the two men circled, stepping like cats, watching for an opening. Then, with a rush, Jack Armstrong closed in to grapple. Abe gripped Jack with a grasp like nothing the latter had ever known. Armstrong tried to get a crotch hold and failed, tried eye-gouging and ear-biting and missed. He was rapidly getting bested. Then, in desperation, he brought his heel down hard on Lincoln's instep.

At this sudden agonizing spurt of pain, Abraham, in fury, lifted his opponent in the air. Kicking and flailing, Jack Armstrong felt himself lifted higher, higher . . . by the man who could carry a chicken shed across Josiah Crawford's barn lot . . . by the man who could heft a covered wagon out of a mud hole . . . by the man who could shove a flatboat off a Mississippi snag . . . and was flung full length.

Lincoln, panting, hands on hips, legs spread, his foot still a flame of pain, watched. Jack Armstrong didn't get his breath back at once. He lay there, gasping like a stranded catfish.

The Clary's Grove boys, at the downfall of their champion, gave a concerted howl of wrath.

"Foul!" they screamed. "Lincoln pulled a foul! Get him, men!"

They closed in on Abraham. He was backed against the wall of the store and stood at bay.

"That was no foul!" roared Abe, thoroughly aroused. His usually placid disposition quite lost in the unnecessary battle, he knocked about him with his fists, holding the attackers at arm's length.

"Come at me one at a time and I'll lay you out! Come on like real men—I'll take you singly, not in a mob!"

The men retreated a few steps. Jack Armstrong, meanwhile, slowly gathered himself together, shook his head several times, as if to clear it, and stood on his feet, swaying a bit but still powerful. He faced Abe, who had no takers on the one-at-a-time business.

Suddenly, with a grin, Jack Armstrong strode toward his opponent, hand outstretched.

"Shake, Lincoln!" he said cordially. "I never yet found a man could lay me out, and you done it like I was a sack of middlin's. Any man can lay me out like that, I got to admire him. Anyway, I fouled you, and I apologize."

Abraham's big hand shot out, and he gripped Jack's calloused paw.

"You're as strong as I am," he vowed. "Another minute and you'd have done the same to me. I declare this match a draw, and all bets called off!"

The crowd, suddenly affable, yelled and threw hats into the air. Jack and Abe grinned companionably at each other, friends forever. As the two strongest men and best fighters of New Salem shook hands on a hot, dry, dusty September day, Denton Offutt and William Clary took back their bets, silently and with no comment.

In Jack Armstrong and the Clary's Grove boys, Abraham Lincoln found unswervingly sturdy backing and faithful friends. Their attitude toward him was an odd one and it embarrassed him no little. They accepted him as their physical equal, yet seemed to feel he was different from themselves. He was kind and gentle, yet strong as the strongest and supreme in a fight. In a profane period, he used no profanity. In a time of heavy drinking, he touched no liquor. Instead of ridiculing these traits, as they did in the case of most of the earnest members of the Temperance Society, which was trying to combat the evils of strong drink in New Salem, they felt astonishingly protective and even fatherly toward Lincoln. The Clary's Grove boys vowed they would defend him against all enemies and accusers, would rally to his cause whenever he needed help. It had all started there on the hilltop after that fight with Jack Armstrong. In a way, Abe was rather glad it had happened.

As winter again dropped snow on New Salem hill and the drifts heaped high, so that folk feared a repetition of the dreadful Winter of the Deep Snow, it was beginning to be obvious that the Offutt store was not going to be a thriving concern.

The Herndon-Berry store, down on main street of New Salem was doing a better business than Offutt's, and so was Reuben Radford, who had taken over the Chrisman store. But it was Sam Hill, in partnership with John McNeil, who was the most prosperous from the very beginning. Hill managed to stay that way while other businesses failed about him like flies in the first frost. Even when McNeil sold out and went East, Hill's prosperity continued.

Abraham was little disturbed by the scanty business which came to Offutt's store. He was merely a clerk, and a poorly paid one at that. Small trade to Lincoln simply meant more time in which to read. There were far more books available in New Salem than in any place in which he had lived before, and Mentor Graham, the schoolmaster, was helping him, nights, on things he didn't understand.

Denton Offutt often was away on some mysterious business of his own. Abraham Lincoln and Billy Greene slept in the store, their heads pillowed on bolts of calico, a buffalo robe spread over towsacks filled with cornshucks under them, and another buffalo hide over them. The two talked long into the night. With a smoky tallow candle, or by the light of the fire only, sometimes Abraham studied from Kirkham's *Grammar*, which Mentor Graham had suggested he borrow from John C. Vance.

There was only one copy of this priceless book in New Salem, and that was the one from which Graham taught his advanced pupils who were preparing for college, so that he could not very well loan it out. Getting wind of that other copy, Abe set off and walked six miles out over the prairie to borrow it. He had his nose in his prize almost all the way back home again, fascinated yet appalled by what he read. There was so confounded much he didn't know!

It had all come about because Mentor Graham had been arguing with Lincoln about education.

"Reckon I have enough learning for anything I'm ever likely to do," said Abraham, in a fit of melancholy, complaining about the futility of existence.

"No, you have not!" contradicted the peppery schoolmaster, who seldom smiled, almost never laughed, but whose grim exterior hid one of the kindest hearts in Sangamon County.

"You need mathematics, and you need a bout with a speller, and most of all you need to learn grammar. You'll have to learn how to think out your sentences so that they sound best and make the clearest impression on your hearers. Don't use two words when one will do. Get the true meaning, Lincoln, and then work until you express it most effectively."

"Well, but—"

"Don't interrupt, I'm not finished," snapped Graham, glaring at him from under reddish eyebrows. Abraham subsided.

"It seems to me," went on the schoolmaster, "that you ought to get a public position of some sort. If you do, you'll need better diction than you have now. You're full of a backwoods twang, and you use expressions which are all right in a place like New Salem, but not out in the world. You do get on well with people. I hear that folk come to you to write out legal documents and papers for them. But you can express yourself better than you do; you'll just have to study more. I'll help you."

So Abraham studied. He found grammar amazingly interesting,

but at times extraordinarily difficult. Sentences had a way of getting tangled, words of getting misspelled, phrases of getting misplaced. After a bout of parsing sentences and memorizing verbs and nouns, he'd hand the book to nineteen-year-old Billy Greene, who was planning to go to the new Illinois College soon, and it was Billy who asked questions while Abraham recited.

Sometimes Lincoln had a long and wonderful evening over at Mentor Graham's big brick house, reviewing what he'd learned, philosophizing, talking—talking until tart Mrs. Graham reminded them for the dozenth time that it was late enough to stop their eternal clacking.

Abraham got hold of books of higher mathematics. His analytical mind delighted in the order and reason revealed behind the laws of the universe. He devoured these books as if they were food, as if he were starving . . . and looked for more.

No matter if he had so few months of formal schooling; his mind was ready for bigger things and he felt he could not get enough. He took in history and Shakespeare by the volume and ground his way through the spelling book until he knew most of it by heart. He read Thomas Paine's *Age of Reason* and *The Rights of Man*, and felt his mind fermenting with new thoughts and the excitement of a new philosophy as Paine conceived it.

It was an exhilarating way in which to spend a long, cold, snowy winter, with not much business coming to the store. Lincoln joined the Debating Society and attended meetings of the Temperance Society, which the intellectuals of the community—young Doctor Allen, James Rutledge, John Camron, the Reverend John Berry, Judge Bowling Green, Mentor Graham and several others— fostered and brought into being.

By this select group, the rough exterior and awkward ways of the newcomer were made welcome. They expected him to get up and tell funny stories, but when he gave his first speech before the Debating Society, the critical audience was considerably surprised, all but Mentor Graham, who knew Lincoln's capabilities. Abraham had worked on his speech for some time and hoped he would give a good account of himself. His nervousness, however, melted away when he got started. He thereupon presented a well-thought-out, logical argument for the improvement of the rivers, a pet subject.

After that, his new friends in the Debating Society made plenty of opportunities for Abraham to speak. That winter, they discussed not only river improvements and President Jackson's trouble with the national bank, but went into the touchy subject of the abolition of slavery and the annexation of territories as states, and whether or not slavery should be permitted in the new districts. The affairs of the nation were argued out and settled in the comfortable log cabins of New Salem in the winter of 1831-32. They might not have actually settled anything, but Abraham felt that he was learning how to talk better in front of people, how to organize his thoughts and not get flustered. If for nobody else, he figured, the winter with the Debating Society was of tremendous value to him, at least.

CHAPTER SIX

IN JANUARY, 1832, a letter reached the postmaster of Springfield. It had come all the way from Cincinnati by the mail stage and it was from Vincent Bogue, who owned a mill on the Sangamon River. This river, Bogue declared, was an ample and neglected artery of trade, connecting the midlands with the Illinois and Mississippi Rivers. He proposed to bring a steamboat down the Ohio to the Mississippi, up the Mississippi to the Illinois, and up the Illinois to the mouth of the Sangamon, thence to navigate as far on that stream as was feasible, probably to his own Bogue's Landing, near Springfield.

"I shall deliver freight from St. Louis to the landing on the Sangamon River, opposite the town of Springfield, for 37½ cents for a hundred pounds!" This was less than half the rate charged for hauling freight on land.

News of low freight rates; steamboats coming up the Sangamon; direct connection with ports of America—and Springfield, New Salem, Sangamo Town and other Sangamon County communities suddenly were electrified at the prospect of what the future held for them.

"They'll need men to clear the river so's a steamboat can navigate," commented Jack Kelso. "Just think, it'll pass New Salem, if the water is high enough so it can clear the dam. I never could see any sense in damming navigable streams, anyway, even though it does make better fishing. I should think James Rutledge would've had better sense. With the water high, though, I reckon they'll make it."

"I'd sure admire to be one of those to clear the way," mused Abraham Lincoln in a pleasant glow of anticipation.

It had been his dream, ever since he spoke at the Fourth of July celebration in Decatur, two years before, to find a way to make the Sangamon River navigable. It was a long enough stream, rambling far inland from the Illinois and connected by means of that stream with the whole vast Mississippi Valley and the trade routes from the East Coast, not to mention all the Ohio River trade.

But the Sangamon was a river of extremes. It was quite often miserably low in summer, iced in winter, and it had more than its share of snags, sandbars, overhanging branches, trees fallen into the water and multiple twists, turns, forks and violent eddies. Again, it could be very broad, deep, full and smooth.

A big steamboat could not be expected to navigate such a stream, but a small-to-medium one could. If only the coming steamboat, the *Talisman*, were not too big! And so, for two months, Abraham Lincoln dreamed about a steamboat coming up the Sangamon River, opening the land to new trade, new life and new adventure. Everyone in the valley knew a growing excitement. Steamboat trade would bring reliable transportation into a land which, during much of the year, was often impassable, with mud roads or none at all. The world was coming to the doorsteps of cabins in the back country of Illinois!

On the strength of this prospect, new settlers came into the area. New towns were hastily laid out. Land values tripled overnight. Merchants in small towns of the valley began to advertise the fine merchandise they were about to offer to eager customers, and farmers were planning to send produce to market at a cost of less than half that of land travel. Meanwhile, the Sangamon Valley, together with Abraham Lincoln and Vincent Bogue—the latter having sunk all his money and much of his creditors' cash in the venture—anxiously waited for the snow to go off and the ice to break up in the river.

With the brown waters still partly frozen, but with bluebirds caroling in the glossy carmine twigs of the willows and the breath of spring in the air, the *Talisman* arrived at Beardstown. Ten miles upstream from this port, the Sangamon was riding high with foaming melt-water from the hills.

At the mouth of the Sangamon, where the willows were awash in the high water, the steamboat was met by a flatboat-load of men from Springfield and New Salem—Washington Iles, Thomas Neale, Edmund Taylor, Abraham Lincoln and others, all equipped with long axes, enthusiasm and muscles. They had drifted down the river, breaking through the remaining ice, cutting branches from overhanging maples and sycamores, chopping out snags and letting them float free. It was hard work, especially clearing away shoals which lay across the river and were all but invisible beneath the surface.

The *Talisman* was ready to start. Her chimneys gushed black smoke, the engines thudded and roared, steam hissed, bells rang, roustabouts called back and forth. The river-clearing crew, triumphantly aboard the steamboat, watched dozens of enthusiastic men and boys, afoot or on horseback, follow a distance along the tangled banks as the steamboat slowly, very slowly, made her cautious way into the river.

In the backwoods of the Pecan Bottoms, people living in crude shacks and in giant hollow sycamore logs came outdoors hesitantly, like wild creatures, half afraid of the strange white monster shoving noisily up the river. Many of them had never seen a steamboat before and shuddered at its smoke and foam and size and noise. A big craft painted white—at least she looked mighty big on the Sangamon—the sidewheels smacking the water—it was a marvelous sight!

But the uneasy pilot, Mr. J. M. Pollock, nervously twirled the big wheel as his charge ground along, making four miles an hour when she was lucky, moving upstream on a strange river which had never before known the paddlewash of passing steamboats nor the mellow tones of whistles calling.

There was enough water over the dam at New Salem to carry the steamboat easily and safely past. The entire population of the town flocked to the waterfront in wonderment and delight and crowded the narrow porches of the mill in order to see better, as the boat tied up at the ferry landing. Lumber from the mill was loaded on the lower decks, the whistle blew, bells clanged, echoing against the hill, and the *Talisman* was on her way.

Several hours later, the people at Sangamo Town upstream, notified by boys posted at points along the river, watched as the steamboat hove into view around the bend, slid easily over the well-flooded limestone of Roll's Ford and moved on toward Springfield.

Seven miles from that town, at Bogue's Landing, the steamboat tied up. Her pilot hesitated, had in fact refused, to go any farther. He was already in a bad state of nerves at what he had done to bring his craft up the Sangamon. If the water should begin to fall, he knew he would never get the *Talisman* out alive. She would struggle vainly to escape and would leave her white bones on the river's muddy bars and shores, forever lost in the forest, far from deep, wide open water.

Oblivious to danger, the people staged a great celebration in Springfield. A reception was held for the boat's officers and for society lights of the area. A noisy and enthusiastic dance was staged at the courthouse. Local drinking establishments did a thriving business. The goods which Captain Bogue had brought from Cincinnati and St. Louis were sold to the eagerly waiting merchants. Quite a few of them, however, bought on credit. Everyone heralded the opening of a new era of prosperity, brought to central Illinois by the river.

Abraham Lincoln, with several days' holiday from Offutt's store, stayed in Springfield, got acquainted with as many people as he could, attended the dance and altogether had an exhilarating time.

And the brave white *Talisman*, lying at the landing, daily tugged harder on her mooring ropes, which grew more and more taut. The water was dropping.

"I'll never make it!" vowed Pilot Pollock, seeing how mud and sand bars lay exposed which hadn't been visible on the upbound trip. "I'd never tackle the job in a thousand years! Get somebody else. I'm a deep-water man. I can't pilot a steamboat in this little ditch, in a trickle a cow can wade across and not get her tail wet!"

Pilot Pollock was exaggerating, but anyone could plainly see what was happening to the river, could figure what might surely happen to the steamboat.

Captain Bogue, in desperation, asked for help. He could see the profits of his venture rapidly vanishing in ruin.

"Rowan Herndon of New Salem is a bang-up pilot," someone recommended. "He could take that-there steamboat acrost a pasture in a heavy dew. But there's plenty of water left in that old river. You should ought to see her in August!"

"You ever piloted a steamboat before?" asked Bogue of Herndon, who, with Lincoln and a good many other New Salem men, was in Springfield for the celebration and was handy when needed.

"Well, not on the Sangamon, I'll allow," Rowan Herndon grinned, "because there ain't *been* no steamboat before on this here river. But I can guarantee you I'll get your steamboat to Beardstown, if I have to tote her on my back. But I'll need some help."

"Who you want? Name him and we'll get him!"

"Well, Lincoln's had a lot of experience on the rivers. He'll do as good a job as I will, if not better. We could take it in shifts."

And so Abraham Lincoln, on that fine March day, was signed on as assistant to the temporary pilot. Together they maneuvered the steamboat down a rapidly narrowing stream which was becoming more and more untrustworthy, dropping fast, as that river does when its spring crest is past. Lazy waters and mud bars made progress slower and slower. The boat barely scraped through, yet kept afloat.

Captain Bogue was in despair. Mr. Pollock devoted most of his waking hours to solace in strong drink and had bad dreams at night. Sometimes, when he and Bogue dared to look outside the cabin windows, it seemed to them that the *Talisman* was struggling through the forest with not a drop of water in sight.

But there was still enough . . . still enough. The steamboat crawled along at four miles a day . . . a day, not an hour. Nights, they tied up. The passengers did their best not to be bored or worried about the outcome of the voyage.

Ahead, like the walls of Troy, lay New Salem dam. This nemesis of boatmen, a sturdy dam made of wooden cribs filled with a thousand wagon loads of rock hauled from the quarry near New Salem, had caused Abraham Lincoln considerable anguish, both mental and physical, only the year before. It looked to him as if it was going to do it again, only more so. For this was no flatboat which could be lightened by taking off cargo, nor assisted by boring a hole in the bottom to let out water. The *Talisman's* cargo had already been unloaded, back at the landing. Removal of the passengers would not lighten her enough to matter. That dam looked high as a wall.

The crew looped a line around a sycamore to tether the boat while Lincoln went ashore. He conferred with John Camron, who, with James Rutledge, still owned the mill, though Denton Offutt had been renting it. Abraham didn't relish what he had to say. Camron wouldn't like it so well, either.

"Say, John—" Abe began unhappily, hitching up his jeans. People were gathering on the riverbank again, to watch the steamboat, which looked like a great, snowy duck on the narrowing stream. She was an impossibly beautiful, heartbreaking sight. Hope and despair, promise and failure, lay contained in her shapely form.

"John," went on Abe bluntly, to get it over with, "we've got to tear down part of your dam to get this steamboat through. I know you won't think kindly of it, but we sure can't track her off across the fields on any short cut to Beardstown and she can't stay here till the river rises again, which may not be until next fall. I'll be careful how I take down the dam and will rebuild it for you as good as new afterward."

John Camron frowned. He didn't like the idea of damage to his milldam, but he knew as well as Abe did that only an improbable rise in the river would float that big critter over the dam.

"Well, all right, Lincoln," he sighed. "I reckon you know what you're about."

And so the *Talisman* finally was enabled to move slowly and ponderously through the break in the dam. She was tied up again below, so that Abraham and the men could reset the cribs and stones, then ground and scraped her way downstream into the broader reaches of the Sangamon. Thankfully, all on board saw the steamboat slide into the deep waters of the Illinois River and head for the port at Beardstown.

Rowan Herndon and Abraham Lincoln were each paid forty dollars for their services. This looked like a fine lot of money, especially to Abraham, whose pay from Mr. Offutt was not only small but highly irregular.

It was then, in the peaceful, wet Illinois springtime, with the Offutt store rapidly failing, with the *Talisman* gone and, along with her, the prospects of successful steamboat trade materializing on the Sangamon, that the Indians in northern Illinois started a commotion which was felt in New Salem.

The Black Hawk War had begun!

CHAPTER SEVEN

WAR, STEAMBOATS AND POLITICS—that was the three-way trend of talk in Illinois in 1832.

It was in March that Abraham Lincoln, for lack of anything else to do, decided to take a try at politics. This was about as foreign as any other subject to him, but he figured he could learn if other men could. His entry into New Salem had been marked by an election, and political talk had whiled away endless hours during the winter.

Those arguments in general ran for or against the Jackson party. Partisans were violent in their opinions, and many a steamed-up argument turned to emphasis with fists when it came to holding out for Jackson or Clay, Democrats or Whigs. The Democrats were the common people, the men who had to work for their living and who were outspoken for that hearty man of the people, Andrew Jackson. The aristocrats were Whigs. They favored Henry Clay.

It was somewhat startling to his friends when Abraham Lincoln came out as a Whig, for Clay and his policies—Abe Lincoln, who had always been poor, had always labored with his hands, and who had never been affiliated with aristocrats!

"How come you're a Whig, Lincoln?" asked Billy Greene, curiously.

"Well, I don't hold with Andy Jackson, not one little bit!" replied Abraham rather sharply. "He may be an all-fired big military hero, but just because a man wins a battle down in the cypress

57

swamps of Louisiana doesn't mean he's going to be good in politics or running the nation."

"What about Washington?" put in Billy. "He was a mighty fine general and fought a good war. Won it, too, like Jackson."

"Well, George Washington wasn't like other men," defended Lincoln, who idolized the latter. "He was as good a president as he was a military man, which is saying a good deal, but Jackson sure isn't a Washington! Besides, he hasn't played fair with the Indians. And he's out to destroy the United States bank, too!" Lincoln strode in irritation to the window, then came back.

"I hear he claims that poor people, who have nothing and likely know less, can rule the United States as well as, if not better than, the aristocrats who've been doing it since the beginning!" he added acidly.

"That sounds kind of funny, coming from you, Lincoln." Billy grinned up at him. "You aren't exactly an aristocrat yourself, meaning no offense!"

"That's no news to me," agreed Abe drily. "But I've seen men like me with a whole lot less education even than the smattering I've got, and with a whole lot lower moral standards, who have political notions. I'd hate to see some of them taking on the control of our government. I shudder to think of it!"

"You're just biased because Clay's from Kentucky and so are you," drawled Coleman Smoot, coming in and leaning on the counter. "Give me a piece of cut plug, will you, Abe? And the old lady she wants a spool of white sewin' thread and a half a pound of tea, and don't you weigh your thumb with that there tea, boy, you old Whig, you!"

Coleman Smoot laughed at Lincoln's injured look. He was noted for his strict honesty in weighing and measuring out the exact amount and the correct change to everyone.

"Well, I'm right proud to be from Kentucky," said Abraham, slicing off the chewing tobacco and handing it over, "but if Andy Jackson was from my home county and neighbored with my family, or even was kinfolk, I still wouldn't be partial to him nor hold with his policies. No, sir! That be all, Mr. Smoot?"

ABRAHAM LINCOLN AND BILLY GREENE SLEPT IN THE STORE, THEIR HEADS PILLOWED ON BOLTS OF CALICO. . . . WITH A SMOKY TALLOW CANDLE . . . SOMETIMES ABRAHAM STUDIED. . . .

IN THE BACKWOODS OF THE PECAN BOTTOMS, PEOPLE . . . CAME OUTDOORS HESITANTLY
. . . HALF AFRAID OF THE STRANGE WHITE MONSTER.

"Why don't you go into politics, Lincoln?" asked Smoot, pocketing his purchases. "Way you can talk, you'd be ahead of most of the candidates, all except that Peter Cartwright. But he's a preacher and a Methodist one at that, and you can't beat them as talkers."

"What'd I run for?" asked Abe blankly.

"Why, for a seat in the State Legislature down to Vandalia, likely," replied Smoot, as if surprised at his friend's ignorance. "No use startin' low on the ladder. There's twelve men from Sangamon County runnin'. Might as well make it thirteen, though it might be an unlucky number, at that. The bad luck could be for some other one of the thirteen, maybe, and not you. Never can tell."

The idea was new and daring. Abraham Lincoln from the backwoods of Kentucky and Indiana and Illinois, setting himself up to the Illinois State Legislature! It might not be a bad idea. No harm done to try. However, Sangamon at that time was the biggest county in Illinois and covered a territory twice the size of Rhode Island. It might take him a while to get around and talk to enough people so they'd know he wanted their votes. Abraham mulled over the idea. He never decided anything very quickly.

"Seems like I'm so tall, it takes an idea a long time to run the length of me and make up its mind what it's going to do and be, if anything," he joked, when people tried to hurry him into decisions.

One day he went over to Mentor Graham's schoolhouse, which was also the Baptist Church, up in the woods on the hill south of the village. Bill Greene was left in charge of the store.

The weather was mild and sweet for March. Down in the muddy place by the creek where he crossed the log footbridge which the school children used, Abraham discovered fresh raccoon tracks. A black butterfly with ragged yellow borders on its wings flitted in a shaft of sunshine. There were scarlet cup mushrooms poking out like brilliant flowers from beneath damp old oak leaves and fallen branches on the ground, and a hermit thrush, on its way north, flew away from the path as the tall young man climbed the hill.

It seemed that the coming and going of the steamboat had brought spring for certain.

There still was some sap dripping into the sugar buckets hung on the maples up the hill. Abraham paused a moment to sip the thin, sweet water from a tube made of elder with the pith bored out and then went on. The sugaring time was really past. It had ended two weeks before, when there was still snow on the ground, warming days and freezing nights to make the sap rise. For days, the fragrance of boiling sap turning into syrup, and of syrup turning into sugar, had been in the air. The sap still was dripping, but now it was rising strongly through the trees, to give life to twigs and buds.

"Welcome, Lincoln," said Mentor Graham, looking up soberly from his book. School was out, but he had stayed longer than usual in the peace and silence of the empty schoolhouse, before returning to his evening chores, to the noisy houseful of children and to his nagging wife. "Sit down."

The seat offered wasn't especially comfortable. The puncheon benches which the pupils used were hard and rough, but Abe guessed you didn't go to school for comfort. When he folded down on one, he had trouble with his knees, too.

"Can't stay long, and you'll be wanting to get home to supper, but I've got a problem," began Abraham, getting at once to the point. "I know you can help me out—you and maybe Judge Green.

"Folks have been flattering me by asking me to go into politics, run for the Legislature, and I don't know what all. Maybe they're only joshing, but it might be a few of them really do think I could make some sort of show, like the jaybird did when he found a mess of peacock feathers. Anyway, I kind of thought I might give it a try, seeing as how Mr. Offutt's store doesn't look too flourishing, as you might say, and I may be out of a job just any day now. You reckon I'm crazy to think of going into the Legislature, provided anybody'd vote for me, with the little education and experience I've got?"

It was an involved speech. Abraham Lincoln sat back with his long arms around his knees, rocking back and forth a bit, watching the schoolmaster's reaction. He'd hate to be laughed at for his pains.

Mentor Graham's long, sensitive face lightened. You wouldn't exactly say that he smiled, but his face cracked a bit.

"Well, now you may think you aren't equipped for the job," he began, "but I should say from what we've thrashed out this winter that you are well on your way to knowing more than a little. Probably a great deal more than a lot of men aspiring to higher office."

"You think I'd have a chance?"

"As much as any man, I should say," agreed Graham noncommittally, "but you may not get as far as you think. People praise up a candidate whom they like, but you never, never can be sure how they are going to vote until the ballots are counted. You're a Whig, aren't you? Mighty few around here. Mostly Jacksonian Democrats and they'd think twice before voting for you, especially those biased "whole-hog" Jackson men. The "milk-and-cider" Democrats, though—well, you never can tell about them. They're likely to be swayed by whichever man catches their fancy, which may be you. Go ahead, my boy. You'll have my vote, at least!"

"Thanks, Graham!" said Abraham, getting up to shake the teacher's slender, calloused hand. "Now that that's settled, I'll need some help in writing out my platform. Since I don't have any great and influential men to back me, I've got to run on my own merits, I reckon, such as they are."

Written out carefully in Lincoln's best hand, the result had looked rather impressive. This was duly carried in person, on a borrowed horse, to Springfield. It was inserted in the pages of the *Sangamo Journal*, where it was more astonishing to view in print.

Judge Bowling Green had asked Abraham what he stood for, expecting something vague, or maybe pretty high-flown, but he and Graham were surprised at Abraham's concise reply.

"I'm for state-wide education that's paid for by the state, and free to everyone. I think the usury laws ought to be amended so people don't have to pay so much interest on borrowed money.

And I sure do want to see the Sangamon River improved so there can be trade and traffic on it clear to Decatur."

He had ended the letter by saying:

"Every man is said to have his peculiar ambition. Whether it be true or not, I can say for one that I have no other so great as that of being truly esteemed by my fellow men, by rendering myself worthy of their esteem. How far I shall succeed in gratifying this ambition, is yet to be developed. I am young and unknown to many of you. I was born and have ever remained in the most humble walks of life. I have no wealthy or popular relations to recommend me. My case is thrown exclusively upon the independent voters of the county, and if elected they will have conferred a favor upon me, for which I shall be unremitting in my labors to compensate. But if the good people in their wisdom shall see fit to keep me in the background, I have been too familiar with disappointments to be very much chagrined."

Lincoln had had little time to admire his efforts or to do anything more to further his cause. The Black Hawk War was more important at the moment. As he departed for the field of battle, he wondered briefly if all that to-do about a platform would be a waste, after all. If he never came back alive from his encounter with the Indians, it would have been a silly thing indeed, but maybe a suitable epitaph, at that—

I have no other ambition so great as that of being truly esteemed by my fellow men, by rendering myself worthy of their esteem.

What better sentiment could any man ask to be carved on his headstone? With this melancholy philosophy, Abraham had set off to the war.

Well, he hadn't needed a fancy epitaph, after all, at least not yet. He had survived the Indians, the mosquitoes and the camp food, and here he was, back on the political scene, only two weeks before the election in August. His handbills were being distributed in Springfield, New Salem and other communities, but he had been away so long that most of the other candidates, who had wisely remained in the political field, had had all summer in which to go to barbecues and spout speeches and shake hands with the people. It was true that John Todd Stuart, who was also on the slate, had been in the Black Hawk War, too, but Stuart was well-known. He need not be around all the time in order to advertise his cause.

The Reverend Peter Cartwright, another candidate, at a huge revival meeting which attracted several thousand people, had roared fire and brimstone, eternal damnation and the unworthiness of the other candidates, scarcely separating his subjects in his fervor. He dwelt strongly on the fact that most of his opponents were sinners, pagans or worse, and not worthy of being voted for by earnest Christians. He swayed the masses with his thunder. He could mix religion with politics and get people so worked up they would have voted for anyone he recommended, so long as he promised them salvation along with their votes.

"You're going to have to work terrible hard to catch up, Lincoln," warned Billy Greene. "All the rest of the candidates have been stump-speeching and holding forth at barbecues and the like, all summer long. Peter Cartwright's been a-roaring and a-shouting till half the womenfolk at the camp meeting came down with the jerks."

"I know," said Abraham Lincoln tersely, putting on his other shirt and thinking that a haircut would maybe help his looks some, though not much. "And I aim to catch up as fast as I can. I'm no camp meeting exhorter, but I can talk, too!"

Abraham Lincoln set out. He had no horse, so he walked, walked from house to house all up and down Main Street in New Salem, and over to Clary's Grove and Athens, Concord and Sandridge, Indian Point, Sangamo Town and Springfield. Bowling Green lent him a horse for the far places. Lincoln talked to everyone, wherever he went. He talked to the women in the family, too, although they could not vote. They usually gave him a cold drink and invited him to stay to dinner. He talked to farmers in their fields, and while he talked he helped pitch hay or feed the hogs.

There was little opportunity, however, to gather a lot of people together to listen to a speech. Most of the big barbecue rallies were past.

"There's goin' to be a big sale over to Pappsville tomorrow," commented Sam Hill helpfully. "Lots of people goin' to be there. Might be a chance to say your piece."

So Abraham borrowed a horse again and rode to Pappsville. He recognized a good many people in the crowd, but he scarcely knew how to present his cause. Since he came unannounced as a speaker, he could scarcely elbow his way to a box or wagon bed and start in to spout off his merits, just like that. While he was standing there, head and shoulders above the crowd and feeling suddenly timid, lonely and pretty silly, too, to have come so far in the heat, Jack Armstrong, also attending the sale, spotted him.

"Hey, there's Lincoln from New Salem, one of our candidates. Hey, Abe, howdy! Come on and give us a speech. Tell us how you're a-goin' to run the Legislature in this here State of Illinois!"

That was all that Abraham needed. The crowd, grinning, made way for the big, broad-shouldered young man who was working his way to the front. There was a wooden box handy; it would make a good enough platform if it held his weight. He tested it. It would hold.

As he stepped up to the makeshift platform and opened his mouth for his first words, and had in fact begun:

"Fellow citizens—" there was a churning and commotion in the crowd. Searching for the trouble, he discovered his good friend, Rowan Herndon, suddenly flailing out with both fists. Lincoln knew Herndon had had a fight last week; maybe this was a continuation of it, and he hated to interfere until he discovered that Herndon was getting the worst of it. Frontier fighting was not a polite method of settling disputes. It was most frequently a dog-eat-dog attack, gouging eyes, biting ears and noses, attempting to mutilate one's enemy before he mutilated you.

As Rowan Herndon went down, people forgot about the tall young man with the craggy features who had just opened his mouth to address them. They formed a mass about the combatants.

Abraham Lincoln took a flying leap from the box and plunged through the circle. He grabbed Rowan's attacker by the baggy seat of his jeans and the collar of his shirt and hoisted him suddenly into the air. The mighty arms flung the fighter in a graceful arc into the crowd, which parted suddenly, and the man flopped to the dust, limp as an empty meal sack. The others who had joined the fight melted inconspicuously away at sight of the fire in Abe Lincoln's eyes and the power in his hands and arms. No one wanted to tangle with that Lincoln. He helped Herndon up, brushed him off, stanched the blood running from his nose and ear lobe.

"You hurt much, Herndon?" he asked his friend anxiously, wiping blood.

"Nope," assented Herndon, grinning cheerfully. "Looks like you saved me from a real beatin', though, and I do thank you, Lincoln. Now you go on back and give us a speech we can get our teeth into. Sorry I broke in like that."

"Speech! Speech!" brayed the crowd.

Abraham was not much in the mood now. He strode back and mounted his impromptu platform.

"Fellow citizens," he began again, rapidly and concisely, as if it didn't matter much to him. "I presume you all now know who I am—I am Abraham Lincoln of New Salem. I have been solicited by many friends to become a candidate for the Legislature. My politics are short and sweet, like the old woman's dance."

He paused there and looked out over the crowd, into the eyes of the people watching.

"I am in favor of a national bank," he went on, without raising his voice, and the women hushed the children so they could hear. "I am in favor of the internal improvement system and a high protective tariff. These are my sentiments and political principles. If elected, I shall be thankful. If not, I reckon it will be all the same."

He stepped down and the people cheered and clapped briefly, and then went on with the sale. He didn't know, as he rode home in the heat, if he had done himself or the state much good by that so-called speech. Looking back on it, it mortified him to think how it must have sounded, brief and not very meaty. If he'd heard any candidate orate like that in his own cause, would he vote for the man or not? Questioning himself honestly, he rather suspected he might, at that.

August 6, 1832, was election day. It dawned hot and humid, with a bright blue bowl of sky and dust on the horseweeds in the river bottoms. Turkeyfoot grass out on the prairie was so high that a horseman could not be seen as he rode the narrow rutted trails which served for roads, coming to New Salem to cast his vote.

Abraham Lincoln thought it was probably the longest day he had ever spent. By three in the afternoon, he was sure it would never end. The temperature was about a hundred, the afternoon cicadas were shrilling away, the flies were terrible, a rattlesnake was killed under the steps at Alex Trent's house, and half an hour went by which seemed like about a week.

The ballots were duly delivered to Springfield, where they were counted with all the rest of those from Sangamon County and the votes were tallied. Next day, the results came to the uneasy young candidate in New Salem.

He had lost.

If elected, I shall be thankful; if not, it will be all the same, he had said. His words echoed drearily in his mind that night, but he felt very sure that it would not be all the same. He would never be the same, either. Still, he had one consoling thought. Even though he had been beaten by the spouting parson, Peter Cartwright, who could shout the fur off a she-bear at six paces, and by John Todd Stuart who was an aristocrat, Lincoln had come in eighth in the field with 657 votes. His own precinct of New Salem had turned out handsomely for him. Out of three hundred votes cast, 277 were for him. He wondered wryly just who the dissenting twenty-three were.

It wasn't a bad record, really, he consoled himself. Give him a little more time on the next campaign, and maybe he could better that record all over the county. He had at least impressed his name and person upon some of the people.

Abraham sighed and turned over in bed for about the tenth time, then gave up. He went outside and walked, meditating, out under the summer stars where meteors were streaking from the northeast. He came back about two, still terribly wide-awake.

The martins were twittering in the dark, pre-dawn sky, and by half past four the east was beginning to glow and a lightness was coming to the sky, making the trees stand out the blacker. Onstot's cows were moving about in the dew-soaked grass and roosters were saluting the sun. Abraham knew there was no sleep in him. He got up for the day.

There was no doubt of it, Abe Lincoln was going to have to find a job. He couldn't live off his friends forever. Surely something would turn up for an able-bodied man.

His chance came sooner than he expected. He was still overcome with the laziness of no work and the heat and a touch of summer complaint when a change came in the business situation in New Salem.

"Say, Abe," began Rowan Herndon one night at supper, "I've about decided I want to get out of the store business. You want to buy my interest in the Herndon-Berry store?"

Severe-faced, gaunt Mrs. Herndon watched Lincoln's reaction to the proposition.

"Yes, I would, Rowan," he said at once.

"Well—fine, Abe—but, well you got any money?" asked Herndon delicately, as his wife nudged him under the table. He knew pretty well that Lincoln was flat broke, as usual.

"No, I haven't," Abraham answered honestly. "When Mr. Offutt skipped town he sort of forgot to pay me my last wages, not to mention certain other debts of his. But if you'll take my note in payment for the whole, I'll see you get paid, and with interest. My Black Hawk War pay ought to be along soon. You'll trust me, won't you?"

67

"Trust you!" burst out Herndon earnestly, while his wife frowned dreadfully but was ignored. "Abe Lincoln, I'd trust you from here to Jericho. Sure, I'll take your note, and if I can loan you some cash money to get started on, let me know. You'll find Bill Berry ain't much of a businessman; he's his own best liquor customer, I'm afraid. Bill's a good fellow when he's sober; smart, too. I reckon his father, bein' a minister over to Rock Creek, and leadin' the Temperance Society like he done, must be full of grief and despair over that poor boy's transgressions!" Herndon had kept on talking steadily, while his wife made several attempts to break in, with no success.

"Bill Berry's all right," agreed Lincoln quietly. "And I'll do what I can to put him on the straight and narrow."

"Mr. Lincoln!" finally snapped out Mrs. Herndon, her greenish eyes ablaze. "You'll sign that note right now while I'm here to witness it! I ain't lettin' you take my husband's business away from him like that without no proper legal transaction! If you ain't got the money, then sign a note, and I'll see to it that you pay your interest prompt and get the principal paid, too, before you skip town like your boss done!"

"Mrs. Herndon!" roared her mortified and furious husband. "You shut up and keep your nose out of my business! I'll take care of money matters in this house without you insultin' my friends!"

Just like that, overnight and with the magical signing of his name, Abraham Lincoln came up in the world. He wasn't really a penny richer and had just gone considerably into debt, but he was co-owner of a store! In spite of Mrs. Herndon's spiteful remarks and venomous glare, it was a pretty good feeling, although the weight of debt hung somewhat heavily. He would be glad when it was paid off and when he was a free man again. Nevertheless, he could not but feel proud to be a partner in a store. He wished his father could see that. It might give him a somewhat better impression of his tall son.

CHAPTER EIGHT

O<small>N A COLD JANUARY</small> day in 1833, trouble broke loose in New Salem. Matters frequently exploded when the Clary's Grove boys rode into town, although cold weather put a quietus on some of their noisier outdoor activities.

The Saturday horse races were no more, and the loud betting and commotion at the cockpit in the hollow just west of Clary's grocery had ceased. The quiet, frost-tightened rigors of an Illinois winter settled down and New Salem devoted itself to getting in enough wood to keep a log cabin passably warm, at least at the fireplace end of the house.

The women were busy making lye hominy, gritting corn, and frying up pork so that their families would be heartily fed. They were occupied at their spinning wheels and looms, making quilts and nursing sick children, but the men had less to do. They spent much of their time in lounging at Sam Hill's store, in the Berry-Lincoln establishment, at Reuben Radford's store and in Clary's grocery.

They were less likely to stay long at Radford's. He seemed to expect them to buy something, and made pointed remarks concerning loungers and no-goods who had nothing better to do than clutter up a man's place of business. Reuben Radford lived twenty miles away, in Springfield, and had only rented the building, which the Trents had used before him, as a business proposition.

Reuben Radford was a giant of a man, almost as big as Abraham Lincoln, but stouter. He was insolent of eye and overbearing of manner, and he would take sass from no man. He hated the Clary's

Grove boys and the hate was cordially returned. Still, they would come to his store for drinks and frequently imbibed so much that the place was thrown into a turmoil, items were wrecked, and a brawl resulted which usually ended in expensive damage to Radford's property.

In desperation, finally, he vowed that he would limit those notoriously heavy drinkers, as well as all other customers, to no more than two drinks a piece. It might hurt business, but it would save destruction to his store.

For a while after this pronouncement, backed up by a carefully hand-lettered placard announcing the new limit, the Clary's Grove boys did not appear. A heavy snow evidently had kept them close to their own firesides. However, snow or not, a few days later Reuben Radford had an errand in Springfield and off he went, leaving his younger brother in charge of the store.

"I won't be gone long, Jack," he said, putting on his big buffalo fur coat. "You can manage, and if them Clary's Grove boys come in, don't you dast sell them any more than two drinks apiece. More than that, and they tear the place up and I've had enough of that!"

"Well, Ben," his brother said dubiously and uneasily. "I will do the best I can, but I hope I don't have no Clary's Grove customers because I sure don't want to tangle with none of them roughnecks. They'd take me apart with their bare hands and scatter my remainders to the buzzards!"

The youth's worst fears were realized when iron horseshoes sounded on the flint-hard, icy ruts of the road. They clanged through the town and pulled up at the hitching rack in front of Reuben Radford's big store. His was the only one there made of clapboards, not logs. The boy gripped the edge of the counter, his heart hammering, as half a dozen big, brawny, bearded men clumped in, rubbing their cold hands and filling the store with the smells of leather boots, buffalo coats, chewing tobacco, goose grease and unwashed bodies.

"Throw more wood on that there faar, boy," drawled Bill Kirby. "This place is like unto the Nawth Pole. Twenty below zee-ro outside, I make me no doubt, and twenty-five below in heah, eh, boys?"

They laughed briefly at that one.

"Give us a drink, sprout," the men demanded, and the youth, with shaking hands, drew the glasses and set them on the counter. They were tossed off with dispatch and thumped down for a re-fill.

"Another round of that Old Monongahela, my bucko," said Japhet Potter, "and hurry it up. If you don't give us a warm store, we got to find our heat *in*side us. Hah—that's good!"

The Radford boy held on to the counter, waiting. He knew what was coming. The first two rounds of drinks had vanished like snow in July.

"All right, what you waitin' for? Another round!" ordered Tom Watkins, shoving his empty glass forward. "Don't just stand there with your eyes buggin' out like a tromped-on toad-frog! Get goin'!"

"I'm—I'm sorry, sir," quavered the boy, "but my brother told me not—not to serve no more'n two drinks around—"

"Well, now, and ain't that just too bad!" sneered Potter, jutting his hairy jaw close to the boy's terrified face. "You can just tell *Mr.* Radford that we don't aim to limit ourselves, or let anyone who pipes up limit how much we drink. Another round, you young skunk, and fast!"

"I'm sure sorry, sir, but my brother—"

"Oh, blast your brother!" thundered Royal Clary, going around behind the counter and shoving the alarmed youth out of the way. "We'll serve ourselves, then he won't lick you because you didn't mind him like a nice, good little boy! Hah! Here we are, fellows. Drink up!"

Reuben Radford's stock of liquor was fairly large. The Clary's Grove boys were fairly large, too, and had sizable capacities. Before long, the stock of Old Monongahela, *tafia* and rum had been considerably diminished. The Clary's Grovers were getting roar-ing drunk. As Jackson Radford slipped out and ran for help, the crash of crockery sounded like horrid music in his ears, the maudlin songs of the drinkers and the splintering of bottles and jugs pre-

71

senting a hideous accompaniment of wreckage. Pretty soon, a flat-iron sailed through a windowpane, letting in a larger amount of cold air than before, but the Clary's Grove boys were beyond caring for that. They felt plenty warm inside and out now.

One of them tossed a bolt of calico on the fire, however, ostensibly to make more heat, but the smothering smoke billowed up the chimney and into the store.

Then, suddenly finished, coughing with smoke, the wreckers had had enough. Whooping, they ran somewhat unevenly from the ruins and leaped on their cold horses. They set off at a gallop, the men yelling and hollering, into the winter sunset, heading toward Clary's Grove to the west.

By dusk they were riding past the farmhouse in which Reuben Radford was staying overnight with his brother-in-law, George Spears. He heard the racket on the splintering-cold winter night and looked out. He turned quite pale—Clary's Grove boys and on an obvious drunken spree!

He went to bed, but sleep came hard and he made a poor job of it. Before dawn, Reuben Radford threw on his clothes and got on his horse. He urged it through the silent, crystal dawn of a winter morning, heading fast to New Salem.

He need not have hurried. The damage would not have been any greater nor any less, he discovered, no matter when he got there.

In a towering fury, Reuben Radford walked through the almost unhinged door and took a quick survey of the mess. It looked like financial ruin. He walked outside, seething. Some of the men of New Salem joined him to commiserate on his loss.

"I'll sell out this bear-garden to the first man to give me a price on it! Right now, fast as I can! I'm through with New Salem and these confounded barbarians. No law and order, no chance to operate a decent business establishment. I'm through!"

Billy Greene, who had been Lincoln's assistant at Offutt's store and who, although he was only twenty-one, was owner of the store building housing Radford's stock, heard the offer.

"I'll buy it, Mr. Radford," he spoke up bravely.

"You?" echoed Radford, with a brief laugh at the round-faced youth. "All right, how much, Sonny?"

Billy Greene, who knew something of the store business and who was far from stupid, knew exactly what he was about. His pink and white face might give him the look of a cherubic child, but his mind was keen and level. He got off his horse and went into the store. The bolt of calico was still smoking furiously and this made him choke, but he saw what he needed to see. There was a mess, to be sure, but not a great deal of actual destruction. Spilled molasses can cause an awful smear, but it washes up fairly easily. Things were overturned, crocks and jugs were broken, but not a great deal else was destroyed.

"I'll give you four hundred dollars as she stands," Bill Greene offered, and meant it. Not that he had four hundred dollars, but it would come in due time, perhaps. All he had now was twenty-three dollars cash, and that was being saved for college.

"Sold!" cried Radford.

Bill Greene paid Reuben Radford the twenty-three dollars and signed two notes at $188.50 each. The transaction was scarcely completed and the ink dry before word got to Abraham Lincoln that Billy Greene had actually bought out Radford. Since this piece of information was hardly credible, Abraham had to come to find out the truth of it. He located Billy Greene at the store, looking over the dismal scene of destruction.

"Well, so you're going to be my competitor, are you, Billy?" he began, looking over the confusion and avoiding a puddle of molasses. "Looks like you've got a big clean-up job ahead of you before I can worry about my trade falling off any more than it has already. What happened?"

"Clary's Grove boys, I hear," answered Billy. "Because Ben Radford's brother wouldn't sell them more than two drinks each."

"Must have been quite a celebration," commented Lincoln drily. "Now Billy," he added, "before you do anything else, you've got to have an inventory. I'll help you. We'll make a list of what's here and how much it's worth, so you'll know what you have and how far in debt you've gone, or how much you've made, if anything.

Come on, let's start. Golly, I wish those fellows had left the window in. It's colder than the lee side of Greenland in here. Fill in that broken pane with that piece of board and stuff rags around it, Billy, and I'll haul that calico out of the fireplace and put a decent fire in it. There!"

All the while he was making the inventory, Abe Lincoln was thinking. This stock was worth a good deal, he was beginning to see. The contents of the store outwardly looked bad, certainly, but actually most of it remained in excellent condition. Radford had sold good merchandise; this was quality stuff.

It was, in fact, a whole lot better than that reposing on the dusty shelves of the Berry-Lincoln store across the street.

"Say, Bill," Abraham began, tapping his teeth with his slate pencil, his breath coming in a white cloud in the chill air. "Say, what would you think of selling out to us?"

Bill Greene blinked. Things were moving rather too fast for him.

"How much?" he asked, as Reuben Radford had asked several hours earlier.

"I reckon Bill Berry and I can pay you—let's see now: if my memory serves me about what there is in our till, plus my Black Hawk War pay, we can give you $265 in cash, Billy, and will assume your notes to Radford. If this isn't enough, I reckon Bill Berry's got a horse we can throw in."

"Why that's fine as silk with me, Lincoln," said Billy, somewhat dazed by all this high finance in which he had only paid out twenty-three dollars, yet had bought and sold a store in the process, and now came out with $265 in hard cash in his pocket. There was ample to see him off to college in the fall. "Maybe you'd better ask Bill Berry what he thinks of it before you . . ."

"Oh, Bill won't mind what I do. He'll approve," said Abraham airily, but just the same, he went over to rout out his oversleeping partner and tell him what he proposed. Berry agreed, sleepily. Abraham emptied the cash drawer and poured a lot of small silver and bills into Greene's pocket. Feeling somewhat like a millionaire, William Greene went home to tell his folks about the whole thing. Between breakfast and supper he'd made enough to send him to college! As for Abraham Lincoln, he was poorer than ever and more deeply in debt.

The partners moved their stock from the other store into the newly cleaned up building in which the window panes had been reset, having been brought by Harvey Ross, the mail carrier, from Springfield. The Lincoln-Berry store was the sturdiest and best of the store buildings in New Salem. Its clapboard walls gave it a much more distinguished look than a log structure, and there was a small room off the main part where Abe and Bill could sleep.

Lincoln felt like a prosperous merchant when he surveyed his wares and the new surroundings, though the cash drawer was pretty empty and it was very slow in filling up again. However, competition was less, with Radford gone. Besides, William Clary, irate at the continued opposition to his stock-in-trade by the strong-voiced Temperance Society, was moving to Texas, so that only the Berry-Lincoln store and Sam Hill's prosperous establishment remained to supply the trade of New Salem and its surrounding settlements. Sam Hill was also postmaster, which job, though not lucrative, brought more business to his store.

Other changes had come to New Salem that winter. The Rutledges, meeting financial reverses the autumn before, had sold the tavern to Nelson Alley and had moved out to John McNeil's farm on Sandridge, north of New Salem. The Camrons were gone, too. They had sold the mill.

That winter, old Uncle Enos Short, a Revolutionary War veteran, but spry and spunky for his age, was out turkey hunting. He fired into a flock, killed six, fell down when the musket kicked and broke his leg. He was the talk of the town for days.

In January, Rowan Herndon, in cleaning his gun, which he swore afterward he didn't know was loaded, killed his wife when the piece discharged. Although folk in New Salem were united in admiring Enos Short's accomplishment, they were considerably divided about Mrs. Herndon's tragic death.

"It's my considered opinion," stated one, solemnly, "that Rowan

Herndon wasn't cleanin' no gun when it happened, and it wasn't no accident! Mis Herndon, she had a temper like a white-faced hornet, and I've heard many a tongue-lashin' she's give him, and he handin' back as good as he got. No, that wasn't no accident!"

"He was sure broke up about it, though. Seems like if he done it a-purpose he wouldn't carry on like that, nor cry like a baby over her box at the buryin'. You take notice how sad-lookin' he's been ever since, and swears he's got to get away from the place that reminds him so much of her."

"Well, yes, maybe. Likely he does want to get away—off where it's a mite safer than where he might be convicted of murder!"

"No, he won't be convicted of anything. They've closed the case. They all agree it was accidental."

"Well, be that as it may—"

That winter, things went poorly with the Lincoln-Berry store. For one thing, they didn't sell whiskey by the drink, only by the jug or barrel, as all backwoods stores did. Whiskey was as much a part of the usual stock as it was customary to sell calico over the same counter as the lard, ax handles and rock candy, churns, china and cheese. One was required to have a special license, however, to sell liquor by the drink. It was all right and free in bulk, but to sell drinks on the premises turned the place into a grog shop.

Abraham Lincoln was against this method of dispensing hard liquors. He had refused to get a liquor license, but young William Berry, handsome, educated, but dissipated, felt they ought to sell the stuff.

Abraham protested when Bill was especially insistent.

"It'll give the place a different kind of reputation and won't do either of us any good!"

"It would help business, though, Lincoln," insisted Berry. "We'd do twice the volume if we sold drinks by the glass. I'll see to getting a license, and all you'll have to do is sign it at the bottom and then forget the whole thing!"

And so, somehow, it happened. The Berry-Lincoln store was selling drinks . . . but only when a customer came in, which was not so very often. William Berry, his own best customer, diligently drank up all the profits. A certain desperation and despair overwhelmed him which only whiskey seemed to alleviate for a little while. Abraham was worried about him.

As spring came on, the situation grew worse. Lincoln's frequently morose soul brooded over the inevitable failure he saw looming ahead. Whatever he turned his hand to seemed to fail. First it was Offutt's store and now the Berry-Lincoln store going to the dogs, headlong on the road to ruin. And not only this, but William Berry's drinking and the liquor trade itself worried him night and day.

In April, 1833, Abraham Lincoln knew what he had to do. He sold his interest in the store to Bill Berry, who didn't seem to mind the grinning goblin of impending failure as long as he had plenty of whiskey in which to drown his disappointments. Lincoln, feeling unutterably low in spirits and in funds, wondered what was next.

"Well," he said wryly, out loud to no one in particular, "as the little dog said when he looked at the tip of his tail, 'This is the end!'"

He could have skipped town as Denton Offutt did. Lincoln could have gone off quietly and tried his luck elsewhere and left his creditors holding the notes he had so rashly signed. The great West was waiting for men like him who had made a failure of themselves. The West was big, and a man lost himself easily in its immensity. But New Salem was home. His friends were here, people who were trusting him to pay his debts and who knew that in his honesty he would. He knew it, too, but with what or when he hadn't the foggiest notion. It made him shudder to realize how deeply in debt he had gotten himself, and how many people he owed, and what an astronomical sum it was, with not a stray penny on hand to pay even the interest.

"Well, I've got to get down to work, somehow," he reflected. "There are always fence rails to be cut; fence rails have fed and clothed me before and they can again. Maybe Sam Hill can use a clerk now and then, and—well, something may turn up!"

Only a very short time after this decision, Parthena Nance and Jane Miller had a heated discussion.

"I tell you, Parthena, I will not abide being insulted in Sam Hill's store every time I step in to get my mail!" snapped Jane Miller, hands on ample hips, eyes flashing fire under her scoop bonnet. "Whenever I go, with maybe something cooking on the hearth and I'm in a hurry to get back, there's that insolent Sam Hill waiting on liquor customers hand over fist, while the mail patrons stand around on one foot and then the other, waiting his own sweet time! How you can tolerate the man, I do not see, Parthy!"

Parthena Nance, who was handsome and tall and dark, with a temper of her own, was extremely fond of the craggy-featured, hot-tempered, dashing Samuel Hill, but she could see Jane Miller's point of view. The women who had business at the post office had to wait while the liquor customers were tenderly cared for. It was a rough, tough, odorous atmosphere, and a lady, even a pioneer woman who had learned to put up with a good deal, ought not to have to endure it when she was about her honest business with the United States post office.

"In my opinion," put in Mrs. Onstot quietly, "Abe Lincoln ought to have the job. He's polite and pays attention when you talk."

Jane Miller and some of the other strong-minded women of New Salem got up a petition which they made bold to send all the way to the postmaster at Washington. Time passed, however, and no word came from the East. So much time elapsed, in fact, that the irate ladies felt that their petition had become a hopeless cause or else had been lost along the way.

In May, however, an official letter came from Washington, D.C., informing Abraham Lincoln that he had been selected to take Mr. Hill's place as postmaster at New Salem.

Sam shrugged. He didn't mind. The job of postmaster paid very little, not more than a few dollars a year, and he would really rather be relieved of a somewhat onerous responsibility. Anyway, he liked Abraham Lincoln and was pleased that he had got the job. Goodness knew he needed it.

Abraham read the letter twice and then a third time, and felt a great bubble of delight rise within him. When his spirits were lowest, this letter revived him to life and hope. Even though the job paid so little, all depending upon the amount of mail dispatched and taken in, the esteem bestowed on the village postmaster was a pleasant and useful thing. You were honored when you were postmaster. It was a job with the United States government, and even if it paid less than chopping rails, it actually wasn't very hard or very steady work, while the prestige of the position was eminently great. Not only that, but the postmaster had the privilege of reading all newspapers and other unsealed publications which came into the post office.

"What about your bond?" asked Mentor Graham, scowling out from under his shaggy red eyebrows at the young man whom he loved as a brother.

"Bond?" echoed Abraham blankly.

"It is customary and required for the postmaster to put up a $500 bond when assuming a new post," said Graham discouragingly. "It's returned later, I suppose. Do you have $500?" There was the suspicion of a quirk in the schoolmaster's downward bent lips.

"Five hundred dollars!" It seemed all Abe could do was produce an echo. "It might as well be five million and I'd be as likely to have it. Who would have that much to loan me? You?"

"Not I," replied Graham bitterly. "A schoolmaster is the least paid and the last paid of any man. They compensate me in side-meat and corn and lye soap and all such like, but the cash money is scant and it's all I can do to feed that family of mine. No, I wish I could, Lincoln. Try Sam Hill, or maybe Alex Trent. They are both pretty well fixed."

Abraham was smilingly turned down by Sam Hill, who didn't fancy paying the bond for his successor, though he let him keep the post office in the store. Alex Trent and Nelson Alley, however, decided they would take a chance and between them they put up the amount. Abraham Lincoln signed notes again.

It seemed to him he was always signing more notes, amassing more obligations. He began to think of it as the National Debt and he'd be as likely to have a chance to pay one as the other.

"Well, in spite of getting into debt again," he said to Mentor Graham, "I'm glad they gave me the job. What I can't understand, though, is how I got it in the first place. After all, I'm a Clay man and a Whig, and everyone knows it, and here I'm appointed postmaster under President Jackson himself, who is a Democrat and a loud one. I guess the job just isn't big enough or important enough for anyone to care much one way or the other. Not enough pay for any Democrat to fight for it, I reckon. Just the same, I'm mighty pleased to be postmaster. Somehow, I never expected to rise so high!"

He was not, he soon realized, a very businesslike postmaster. If a letter awaited someone who had not the money to pay for it—postage being paid by the recipient, based on how many pages there were in the letter and how far it had come—he simply handed it over and paid for it out of his own pocket. Sometimes he walked out into the country to deliver a letter in person, if he knew it was special—but since he usually was invited to dinner, this was apt to be worth the trouble. The few receipts which came in were kept in the toe of an old blue sock which Abraham carried home with him at night and brought to the postal desk in Sam Hill's store with him the next morning. The mail carrier, young Harvey Ross, came twice a week to pick up and deliver mail. Between times, there was little for the postmaster to do. That gave him so much more time for studying, or for taking any paying jobs that might come along.

CHAPTER NINE

On a may day in 1833, a young woman in a fashionable blue silk dress with crisp leg o' mutton sleeves and a full skirt tightly belted around her waist, walked deliberately and dramatically down the length of New Salem's Main Street to the post office. Loungers on the porch of Sam Hill's store stopped chewing and sat up. Little boys playing marbles in the dirt paused, knuckles down, as the strange swish of silk brushed past their ears. Silk made a sound which seldom or never had been heard before in New Salem. No calico gown, no linsey-woolsey dress, no alpaca for Sunday best, ever rustled like that, ever crinkled and swished and sang as a lady walked, nor caught the glints of spring sunlight so that the fabric twinkled like a summer night.

If the young woman was aware that people were looking at her, she gave no evidence of being self-conscious or of minding that they looked. She held her head high on its round white neck, carried her straight shoulders well erect, set her kid slippers deliberately one in front of the other, not toeing out as it was thought fashionable to do. She did not mince, nor did she stride like a man, but walked in beauty, poise and confidence, knowing she was making a sensation, knowing the men were looking at her, knowing the women stopped and widened their eyes in envy at her lovely gown and the pale blue bonnet with the rosebuds on the high scoop brim. She knew they saw her pearl-gray mitts—what woman in New Salem wore mitts, but only put on gloves in bitter weather? They eyed her neat black slippers, her parasol, her Cashmere

81

shawl, her unutterably stylish ballooning sleeves.

In a certain shocked silence in which even a catbird in the wild plum bushes was quiet, and in which her precise footsteps sounded suddenly loud on the planks, she closed her parasol and stepped on to the porch of Sam Hill's store. With a fragrance of lavender about her, she walked through the open door.

Abraham Lincoln at the post office desk in the next room looked up and blinked against the light.

"Good afternoon," she said in a clear, sweet voice, smiling ever so slightly at his startled, sun-tanned face. "Do you have any mail for the Abells? And perhaps for me, Miss Owens?"

Abraham Lincoln fumbled through the mail and dropped half of it. Ever since Harvey Ross had come in with the mail that morning, Abraham had wondered who Miss Mary Owens might be.

"Yes, ma'am, there's a letter. It has twenty-five cents due, ma'am. It's come a far piece."

"Thank you," she said and opened her reticule and took out the money. She dropped it into Lincoln's strong, work-coarsened palm. For just a fraction of a fleeting instant, their fingers met. The touch of those finger tips sent a thrill all the way through the young postmaster, leaving him with a curious tingling sensation in his toes.

"My sister wishes me to bring a half pound of black tea, also, sir, and a pound of loaf sugar," she added. Her voice was sweetly southern. No Yankee, she.

Abraham Lincoln got up from the mail desk and moved over to the shop counter, since Sam was out just then. Lincoln was embarrassed at the way he fumbled the tea before he got it properly weighed out and done up in a clumsy parcel. He made a bungle of breaking off the hard white sugar from the blue-paper wrapped loaf. He was still in a state of utter confusion and awe when the splendid vision thanked him prettily and, with a rustling of skirts and sleeves, left the store. She stepped down from Sam Hill's mud-clotted porch, opened her parasol and set off west up Main Street. She picked her way daintily around mud holes where hogs wallowed in calm unconcern of her beauty. If she was staying with the Abells, then she had half a mile or so to walk. The way she stepped out, she would do it easily, Abraham figured.

The men on the porch resumed chewing.

"Glory be!" exclaimed Isaac Golliher, ejecting an arc of brown tobacco juice into the dandelions. "Did you ever in all your born days see the like of that, now?"

"I never in my life seen such fancy fixin's on no female!" ejaculated Ned Potter, batting his red-rimmed eyes at the memory. "I declare, did you hear how she swished, goin' by? Like a wind through a dry cornfield in fall. How come she swished like that there? I never hear my wife makin' no such a noise when *she* walks!"

"Likely you don't," Philemon Morris grinned, "since your woman ain't got no silk gown like that one. It's the silk makes the noise," he explained learnedly. "All the females is crazy for silk gowns so's they kin rustle pretty when they walk. It ain't quite decent, if you ask me, attractin' attention to 'em, like brazen huzzies!"

"You mind your language, Philemon," snapped out tart Mrs. Bowling Green, who had come for her mail. "Miss Owens is a proper brought up young lady and ain't no brazen huzzy, even if she does swish. You ain't noticed her mincin' nor twitchin' as she walked, did you? She carries herself like a lady, keeps her eyes to herself, and I don't want no bold comments from you loafers just because you ain't seen a real lady up close before. Don't show your ignorance!" With this acid comment, she went in and demanded her mail.

She had to ask for it twice before Abraham Lincoln emerged from a trance involving lobelia-blue eyes, curling black hair, skin the color of spring beauties and the electrifying touch of fingers in gray net mitts.

"Yes, ma'am," he apologized absently, giving her the wrong mail.

"Abraham Lincoln, do wake up!" she cried in exasperation. "A body'd think you were sound asleep in the middle of the day. You act as addled as a possum caught suckin' eggs! Pay attention and give me the proper mail, if there is any, and tell me how much is due. I reckon there ought to be a *Sangamo Journal*, too. Or have you *quite* finished readin' it yet?"

She took the sting out of this piece of sarcasm by adding, "By the way, Abe, Squire says come over tonight. Better come to supper and stay the night, if you want. Might as well. Time you two finish discussin' the affairs of the nation and get it all settled how it should ought to be run, it'll be nigh mornin', anyway!"

"Yes, ma'am, thank you, I'd admire to come," said Abe, recovering somewhat. With a few more fumbles, he managed to find all of Mrs. Green's mail and thankfully saw her depart.

He got up from the somewhat dusty, pigeonholed mail desk and sauntered to the door. He leaned one hip against the door frame, casually, hands in pockets, ankles carelessly crossed, while a mud-dauber wasp, busily carrying pellets of mud through the open doorway to a new nest plastered against a shelf, buzzed in irritation as she had to swerve past his head.

"Uh—who was she, boys?"

"You mean Mis Bowlin' Green? Don't tell me you don't recollect seein' *her* before?" countered grinning Sam Hill, who had returned.

"You know who I mean," said Lincoln soberly.

"I heard Mis Green call her Miss Mary Owens, and that's the name she give when she asked for mail."

"No, I mean, where's she from, who's she kin to, and why is such a fine lady in New Salem?"

"Had a southern way of talk," noted Isaac Golliher, remembering. "Heard her plain when she was talkin' to you, Lincoln. Likely she's from Kentucky or Virginia or maybe Nashville. But she's quality, you can tell. Hear how she spoke her words—pretty as a mockin' bird, way she said 'em."

"Yeah, she's quality all right," added Philemon Morris, as if what he uttered was the last word. "No female ever dressed or walked or looked like that in New Salem, meanin' no disrespect to our womenfolk. But, well, I can't see no silk gowns and gray mitts milkin' cows or cardin' wool, or breakin' flax or makin' soap, nor sloppin' the hogs or tryin' out lard, like our females got to do. No, sir. Miss Owens is quality. *She* don't have to do no hard work. She's more'n likely rich as grease and got slaves at home to work for her."

Abraham straightened his hip from the door frame, uncrossed his ankles and in silence went back to the post office counter. He absently finished sorting the mail and noticed suddenly a letter for Mrs. Bennett Abell which he had overlooked in his flurry. A quick flicker of a smile went over his face and vanished before anyone discovered it. He settled down to reading the news in Mentor Graham's *Sangamo Journal*, feet propped higher than his head, until closing time.

The April sunset was sweet and clear over beyond the woods and across the open prairie land west of New Salem when Abraham Lincoln set out. His hair was combed and arranged neatly on his forehead, its unruliness stuck down as best he could manage with grease. His face was freshly shaven, he had on a clean shirt, and the letter for Mrs. Abell was concealed in the pocket of his worn, too-short jacket. He strode west down Main Street, heading for the trail that led to Dr. Abell's farm, north of town.

It was spring on the prairie. The open country was soggy, greening and alive after the April rains. In broad beds like pale blue lake water, the wild hyacinths blossomed. Violets were everywhere, accented by masses of golden-orange puccoon. Old Granny Spears over at Clary's Grove dug the puccoon roots for medicine. In the acres of short, new grass, prairie chicken cocks were strutting in the sunset, heads down, feather tufts elevated like rabbits' ears, bowing, stamping, leaping into the air. He could hear the low, mellow "*ooooooooo*" of the prairie chickens coming pleasantly and a trifle eerily across the sunset. He remembered how, as a boy, he used to make a noise a good deal like that when he blew across the top of an empty molasses jug, and he smiled to himself, remembering. He liked the booming and calling of the prairie chickens. They were even noisier just before dawn.

Where old cattails stood, sand-brown above a prairie pond,

the redwinged blackbirds were giving off their last carols of the
day before they slept. Woodcocks were back. They went hur-
tling off on whirring wings as the tall young man strode past where
they had been probing the mud for worms. High in the clear green
and apricot colors of the sunset, he could see the woodcocks
spiralling madly, uttering their strange "peenting" in courtship
songs. The racketing of frogs and the cool trilling of the toads
filled the sweet spring dusk.

Everything was singing and courting, he thought with a degree
of pleasure in just thinking how loving all the creatures were.
That was kind of the way he was feeling, too . . . bubbly inside,
a bounciness in his step. He began whistling as he walked. The
letter was warm in his pocket.

"Why, it's Mr. Lincoln—do come in, Abraham!" cried Mrs.
Abell when she opened the door to his knock. "We're just sitting
down to supper—we're a mite late tonight, with Bennett helping
the ewes with their lambs this evening. Come join us. We've got
a big pot of dandelion greens that Mary and I picked this morning,
and there's nothing more heartening in spring, I say, than good
new greens to thin your blood. Do stay!"

"Don't mind if I do," said Abraham, pleased. He'd hastily
eaten a chunk of rat cheese and some none too fresh crackers
before starting out when the store closed. Now he carefully
scraped his boots on the doorstep and came in.

"I overlooked a letter that came today, ma'am," he added,
explaining why he was there, "and allowed you might be in a
hurry for it, mail being a scarce commodity around here, usually.
So I thought, since it was my fault you didn't get it, I'd bring it
out to you."

His eyes were roaming the cabin room without finding what he
sought.

"I'm so grateful, Abraham," said Elizabeth Abell, a small, pretty
woman whose husband was well-off. The Abell house had nice
dishes, curtains at the windows and a rug on the floor, a French
rocker made of cherry wood polished to a high shine and a fine
drop-leaf table. Not only that, the Abell house had three rooms, at

a time and in a neighborhood in which two rooms were considered a mighty improvement over the old one-room cabin.

"It's from my aunt in Lexington, I see," Mrs. Abell went on. "Mary will be so glad. Mary," she called, then added to Abraham, "my sister is visiting us—but of course you saw her when she came for the mail."

She was there!

"Mary, I want you to meet Mr. Lincoln, the postmaster. Mr. Lincoln, Miss Owens."

"Pleased to meet you, ma'am, I'm sure," mumbled Lincoln, blindly taking her hand and essaying a brief and awkward bow at the same time. Again he felt prickles at the touch of her hand, clear to his toes. He absently pumped it up and down with vigor until she firmly drew it away.

"It is very kind of you to bring the letter all this way, Mr. Lincoln," she said in her clear, cool southern voice. "If you delivered all the mail in person, it would take most of your time, would it not?"

"Yes, ma'am. No, ma'am," he stammered. "I guess I wouldn't mind. Especially if folks'll ask me to take supper with them, like this." And he laughed, suddenly in possession of his faculties again. "You aiming to stay long, ma'am?" he asked hopefully.

"Oh, until I find it boring," she replied airily, moving about to help her sister put the food on the table. Her strong hands worked capably as she wielded the knife, skillfully cutting the cornbread into precise squares, and dished the fragrant greens into an ironstone bowl. There was sliced ham on a rectangular white platter edged with dark blue, and a bowl of boiled potatoes on which the eaters were to pour ham gravy. There was the clear orange-colored brew of sassafras tea in blue and white cups. It looked like a mighty fine feast to the hungry young man, especially with two handsome women to serve it and preside at the drop-leaf table with its red and white checkered cloth. Dr. Abell came in after washing up from his chores at the barn.

Abraham ate, but he seldom took his eyes away for long from the attractive young woman opposite him. He liked the way her bodice fitted her rounded, rather plump body. She carried herself so well, was so well gowned and groomed, that she didn't look sloppy or as heavy as she probably was—which some other girl might. He thought with an inner grin of Sugar-May Prettiford who always looked as if she were falling apart at the seams. She was big and bulgy in the wrong places and usually had bacon grease down the front of her drab-colored dress, or a hem ripped and dragging.

Miss Owens—well, she was class, she was quality, as he had seen instantly when she came into the store. She wasn't like the usual backwoods girls to whom he had been accustomed. He liked the way she held her shoulders, how cool and intelligent her blue eyes were and how level and merciless they were, too, and yet somehow smiling.

It was an astonishingly short evening. At ten, Abe Lincoln tore himself away from the fascinating company and exhilarating conversation of Miss Owens who, he discovered in gratification, was in possession of an excellent education and could discuss philosophy, literature, French and politics with enviable ease. She humbled him, but she fascinated him anew with every word she spoke. No word was fumbled, none was unsure. He felt that each sentiment falling from those beautifully molded lips was incontrovertible truth and not to be argued with, yet he loved trying to argue, even when he knew she would beat him down every time.

It was not until he was halfway home in the black April night that he remembered with a shock that Mrs. Bowling Green had asked him to supper—and he had clean forgotten it! With an exclamation at his own stupidity, he turned and went across the woods to Greens' house, but found it dark. Well, he'd have to apologize tomorrow.

After that, whenever he had a chance, Abraham Lincoln followed the trail out to the Abells. Grass was growing tall on the prairie, meadowlarks were nesting, the woodcocks had gone on north. The prairie chickens had finished their strutting and booming and had nests in the tall grass, before Mary Owens decided to go home to Kentucky.

Abraham Lincoln was desolated. He had never known a woman like her, had never felt so stimulated in conversation, so entranced by the cool, composed charm of this young woman. Beside her, the conversation of other girls, even sweet Ann Rutledge, who was well educated, too, and was going to go to the Female Seminary in Jacksonville, seemed dull and flavorless. Beside Mary, Ann's prettiness and kindness were dimmed by the other girl's more positive charm and ruthless assertion. Parthena Nance, who was as forthright as Mary Owens, seemed crude and blatant in comparison. None of the New Salem girls, Abraham felt, in his infatuation, could hold a candle to Mary.

"Don't go, you've just come!" he found himself pleading, daring to take one of her hands in his. She let it remain a long, delicious moment, then drew it smoothly away and smiled at him.

"I have been here more than a month, sir, and you will be finding my company a bore if I stay much longer."

"No, never!" he declared with vehemence. "We've so much more to talk about—so much—"

Then, with promise in her blue eyes, she smiled.

"Perhaps I shall come back some day."

CHAPTER TEN

LINCOLN WAS OUT in the woods, laying his broad-ax into oak logs to make fence rails for Squire Green. He was slamming his blade into the wood with a vigor which made the golden autumn woods ring with sound, when a stout figure in homespun approached.

"Hi, Pollard," Abraham called out, wiping his neck and pausing as Pollard Simmons came up. The visitor was somewhat out of breath and perspiring in the unseasonable Indian summer warmth in which Illinois had basked for weeks.

"Lincoln, you got a job! John Calhoun, who's the county surveyor, he says he wants to appoint you deputy surveyor. Ain't that wonderful?"

"Oh, now, Poll, you're joking—or else a mite crazy. Now you begin at the beginning and tell it slow, so I can catch the drift. You say John Calhoun's—"

"He's done sent you word you're to be a deputy surveyor, if you'll take the job!"

"Well, now, that sounds mighty pretty," said Lincoln, still puzzled, "but I'd say at least two things keep getting in the way of my acceptance—one is that the surveyor's job is political, and since Calhoun's a Democrat and I'm a Whig, we don't exactly jibe. Also, he isn't apt to offer someone like me the job, anyway. Besides, I don't even know the first thing about surveying, or the second thing, either. It could be Greek, for all I could tell you about it!"

Pollard Simmons's flat moon face looked blankly up at Abe.

HE GRABBED ROWAN'S ATTACKER BY THE BAGGY SEAT OF HIS JEANS AND THE COLLAR
OF HIS SHIRT AND HOISTED HIM SUDDENLY INTO THE AIR.

SILK MADE A SOUND WHICH SELDOM OR NEVER HAD BEEN HEARD BEFORE IN NEW
SALEM. . . . NO CALICO GOWN EVER RUSTLED LIKE THAT.

"All I know is that Mr. Calhoun he done told me to come and tell you to come to see him if you-all want the job. So I've told you, and that's all I *kin* do!"

Abraham went on splitting rails, but he was thinking hard. That afternoon, he borrowed a horse from Squire Green and rode over to Springfield, to see the tall, dignified and elegant Mr. Calhoun.

"My name's Lincoln, Mr. Calhoun," he began. "Pollard Simmons says you want me—"

"Ah, yes, Mr. Lincoln," said Mr. Calhoun, rubbing his long hands and scrutinizing the tanned, bony, rather melancholy face of the very tall young man before him. "Will you take the job?"

"But, Mr. Calhoun—I—I—why, I don't know surveying," Abraham stammered. "I never surveyed anything in my life except the prospect before me, which is something different again."

"You can learn, can't you?"

"Well, I guess—but I haven't any real education—"

"You don't have to excuse yourself, sir. Lots of us haven't had real educations, as you call them, at least not formal educations in college. You can learn surveying like anything else, if you put your mind to it. It's tough, but interesting, I think you'll find. You can do it. Besides, the pay is fairly good, and with so much land opening up and towns being laid out these days, you'll always be able to earn a living with it."

This latter point, inserted almost casually, was a bigger persuader to learning a new subject than anything else Calhoun could have mentioned. Abraham Lincoln was badly in need of cash. It seemed to him that this was a chronic ailment with him.

"Where can I learn?"

"I'll lend you some books. You'll have to study geometry and trigonometry."

"I've already had some geometry," began Lincoln. "That might help. Mentor Graham, over at New Salem, helped me on it."

"Why, man," exclaimed Calhoun, smiling, "you're halfway there already! You brush up on your geometry. Take these books, and as soon as you think you know the subject and can tell the difference between a piece of land of ten square chains and one of ten chains squared . . . let me know, and I'll send you out on a job."

"By the way, sir," put in Lincoln delicately. "I'm a Whig, you know. Ah—er—will I be required to change my politics?"

"Heavens, no, Lincoln! You continue in your beliefs, and I'll continue in mine, and both of us will keep our peace!"

The rapidity of some events left Lincoln blinking and all but speechless. His mind moved somewhat slowly but surely; it was hard to force it to a quick decision. He had to go over a matter from all angles, studying it out, checking all points, bounding it north, south, east and west, until he knew all the facts. But here he was, quick or not, involved in the art of surveying, with a job waiting as soon as he was smart enough to take it!

He rode back to New Salem with Gibson's *Theory and Practice of Surveying* and Flint's *Treatise on Geometry, Trigonometry and Rectangular Surveying,* some of which he perused as his horse plodded along. The books, tough as the subject matter was, excited him. A long evening of examining them by candlelight, however, finally had him floored.

Next day, in desperation, he took the books and walked across the woods and fields to Mentor Graham's house.

"Graham," he began, thumping his books down on Sarah Graham's polished walnut table, "I've got involved in a problem and have to find a way out of it. Do you know anything about surveying?"

The schoolmaster, who knew a little about almost everything and a great deal about a lot of things, cautiously admitted that he did.

"Well, I'm to learn surveying so I can get a job that's been offered to me. Imagine—me a surveyor! I need some help, though, because this is the Greek-est amount of stuff I ever ran into in my life!"

Lincoln and Graham went to work that evening. Abraham was invited by Sarah to sleep there while he was studying, but precious little sleep he got. Far into the night, the patient teacher and the earnest young man pored over the problems of surveying and higher mathematics. Like so many subjects, Lincoln found that it started out simply enough. It was only a few pages farther along that things began to grow complicated.

He learned that surveying was measuring land by means of a Gunter's chain, which comprised a hundred links totalling sixty-six feet or four rods. He learned that eighty such chains made a mile, that a square chain makes 4,356 square feet, and that ten square chains make one acre, but that ten chains square were ten acres. He learned how you survey a hillside, and how you cross watercourses. He learned how to calculate distances and angles, the declination of the magnetic needle, logarithms of numbers and the solution of triangles. He studied; he figured everything out; he memorized it; he recited and paced; sometimes he thought his head would spin off his neck. He got so little sleep at night that during the day he was red-eyed and bleary and often fell asleep at the counter until jogged awake by a customer.

By the end of six rugged weeks, Mentor Graham also was worn out with the late hours, Sarah Graham was tight-lipped and more acid than usual and Abraham Lincoln looked as if he had endured a six-weeks' siege. He was haggard and had lost ten pounds from his already spare frame. But he had learned enough about surveying to feel that he could take John Calhoun's proffered position and do a comprehensive job of it. He hoped it would be a good-paying one. Goodness knew he needed it!

Before he could do any surveying, however, Lincoln needed some equipment. This, unfortunately, required money, and of this he had but little.

John Calhoun sold him a secondhand surveyor's compass, but he couldn't afford to buy a Gunter's chain. The compass had taken all his cash. Instead, he went to the woods for assistance.

It was on a chill, quiet, fragrant November day that he went down the hill to the river forest below New Salem and hunted for a certain grapevine. Wild grapevines grew to a great size and length in those woods. Nurtured in rich, alluvial bottomland earth, they had, in September, dangled their dark blue fruits high in the tops of the tallest sycamores and maples. Some of the vines were eight inches thick at the base, much too heavy for his purposes. Their trunks were covered with purplish, hairy bark, much fancied by cardinals and catbirds for nest linings.

After an hour's search in the haunting silence of the early winter woods, Abraham located a long, wild grapevine scrambling into a sycamore near the brown river, a grapevine thin enough yet amply strong to be just what he needed. He chopped it off at the base and began to haul it down, hand over hand, wondering how long it would be, and if he would have to splice it.

A twittering flock of bright green, wild paroquets flew out of the sycamore as he pulled at the vine, and he paused to watch. The beautiful little birds were bright emerald in the somber woods, this vivid color accented by the carmine and orange-yellow of their heads. They had been sitting side by side, cosily, along the naked white sycamore boughs, where the afternoon sun warmed them as they fluffed their bright feathers in the chill. They were little disturbed as the grapevine snaked to earth, but only flew to the next tree to arrange themselves as before, side by side, talking to each other, preening, fluffing.

Abraham talked aloud to the paroquets as he worked, since nobody was around to hear him and laugh at his foolishness. Long ago he'd gotten into the habit of conversing with the wild things when he labored alone in the forest. It made it seem more sociable and friendly, less lonely and alone.

He got the vine down and stretched it on the damp, cool leaves on the ground while he measured it carefully with Mentor Graham's foot rule. It was exactly sixty-nine feet long. He cut off the small, straggly end to make it sixty-six feet, a true Gunter's chain. He had read somewhere that a grapevine did just as well as an expensive chain with links, because the vine, unlike rope, would neither stretch nor shrink.

Abraham coiled the unwieldy thing for easier carrying and trudged up the deer trail to the village. He was going to have to get a horse, too. He couldn't always walk; it took too much time to get to a job. There surely wasn't the cash money for one, though, no matter how poor a specimen. But a fellow couldn't always borrow one from his amiable friends; after all, there was a limit to borrowing, and he'd about reached it.

"Thomas Watkins out west of town has more horses than anyone around. They're mainly racers and fancy breeds, but I hear he's got a few old nags, too; might sell one cheap. No harm to try. Tom's near and mean as Laban, but maybe he'll loosen up for you," suggested James Short helpfully.

With this advice in his ears, Abraham Lincoln hiked out the west road to Tom Watkins's place and found that imposing individual, a heavy-browed man, as tall and dark as an Indian, busily currying one of his best stallions. Thin, little Mrs. Watkins was equally busy chopping wood, her breath coming in a cloud in the frosty air. The ax-blade, glinting in the sun, hit the wood with a steady chunking sound. A gray cat rubbed itself ingratiatingly back and forth against her ankles.

Abraham Lincoln would admit to anyone that he was considerably lacking in social graces and didn't know how to act among ladies, but ax-wielding was in his line of trade and he would be the first to assert that no woman could do it properly, nor should she be allowed to try.

Without a glance at Thomas Watkins, who was still lovingly currying the glistening stallion's hide, he went over, split up the kindling for Mrs. Watkins and carried it into the house.

"Needn't to've done that," Tom Watkins commented when Abraham came out again. "Old woman's fit. Got a strong back, good muscles. Never bothered her none to cut up a little kindlin' wood."

" 'Tisn't woman's work, really," said Lincoln equably, admiring the stallion. It reminded him dimly of the Red Duke which his father had had long ago, in Kentucky and Indiana, and which had been sold after Nancy Lincoln died. "Chopping wood is man's work, I always say. But that's neither here nor there, Tom. You got a horse to sell, cheap?"

"I got *no* cheap horses," growled big Tom, carefully running his hand down the stallion's withers. "They're all of them thoroughbreds. Wouldn't have no other kind."

95

"Well, yes, I know, but maybe one of those old nags out in the pasture isn't doing anyone any good. I sure do need a horse mighty bad so I can get my surveying work done."

"Well, that's right, there is one out there you might take. Old but sound in wind and limb. A good mare. How about seventy dollars?" Tom's breath rose in a white cloud in the sharp air. He did not look at Abraham.

"Well, now, that's a mite too steep, Tom," said Lincoln placidly, stroking the stallion's sleek head. "How about forty? And throw in an old saddle and bridle."

"*Forty?* For a mare as good as that *and* a saddle and bridle? She ain't ready for no boneyard! That's a good nag out there," Tom Watkins protested, hurt. "Sixty-five, including the fittings."

"Well, now, sixty-five does seem a little high, maybe. I should think fifty-five might come about right and it's all I can go."

"Make it $57.50 and it's yours," snapped Tom Watkins. "You drive a hard bargain, Lincoln. Hand over the money."

"Oh, I haven't got the cash," said Abe, acting surprised that anyone should suspect that he had that much money at any one time. "But I'll give you my note and pay you later, with interest. With my surveying jobs coming along, it'll be no time before I have the cash."

Thomas Watkins was not in the habit of letting anyone get the better of him in a horse trade; but here he was, like it or not, giving a really good old mare, not to mention an only slightly mended old saddle and bridle, to this sweet-talking thimble-rigger. He wasn't even demanding cash or so much down, but taking Lincoln's note, as if it was worth anything, and he as poor as Peter. That feller's slicker'n a peeled onion, Tom muttered to himself. Just goes to show you can't trust anyone these days.

Thomas Watkins sourly pocketed the note. Abraham Lincoln, with a delicious feeling of accomplishment and affluence, re-membered to examine his horse to make sure Tom Watkins hadn't bamboozled him. With his bony nag saddled and bridled, Abra-ham mounted and slogged off toward home.

Mentor Graham had promised to loan him some old saddlebags.

With that equipment and his compass and grapevine chain; with a new, clean notebook in which to write his surveys and make his maps; and with the knowledge stuffed but lately into his head, Abraham Lincoln was ready.

In six weeks' time he had acquired enough skill and equipment to give him a job which some men went to college to learn. He was on his way to being somebody and making some money at last!

The first job of surveying, which he did carefully, with Hercules Demming carrying the other end of the grapevine chain for him, was for Squire Russell Godbey. They tramped all day through the briars and sand fields, measuring, scrambling through brush, climbing the hard, frozen, snowless January hill. The job should have paid the sum of $2.50, but Godbey was hard up just then for cash, so he gave Abraham Lincoln two dressed deerskins instead.

"Buckskins like them're worth a dollar and a half a piece," Godbey insisted, "so you're really makin' money! You done a good job, and my thanks to you."

Two fly-blown old deer hides for a hard day's work. . . .

"Reckon the squire hasn't heard of the present asking price for buckskins," Abraham said sadly. "Time was, they were worth what he says, but I'll be lucky if I can get seventy-five cents for the two of them. Oh, well."

He gave Hercules Demming half a dollar out of his pocket, the last he had, and rode over to the Armstrongs' near Clary's Grove, for supper. Hannah and Jack were always glad to see him, and he could be sure of a warm meal and a bed in the loft whenever he dropped in. He was tired after that long day in the winter sand hills near the Sangamon, and hungry enough to eat anything the capable Hannah set before him.

"I declare, Abe Lincoln, you look a sight!" exclaimed dark-browed Hannah Armstrong. "You've tracked through briars and brambles all the day long and now look at you—torn to tatters almost, every inch of you. Didn't you notice, Abe? But no, you never do."

Lincoln, who hadn't been especially aware of the fact that he had ripped his pants legs and sleeves into a considerable number of rents and tears, except when a breeze of January air penetrated, glanced down at himself.

"I reckon I do look like the old man all tattered and torn, don't I, young ones?" he asked the children, smiling down at them. "But what's a surveyor to do? It's his business to track around in the brush."

"He don't have to tear himself to ribbons!" contradicted Hannah Armstrong, stirring the hominy. "You think a surveyor's got nothin' better to do than tear his clothes to shreds every time he goes on a job of work? I doubt me that John Calhoun does!

"Now, after supper you take off them pants and put on some of Jack's—no, I guess his won't fit you, at that, with them long legs of yours. I declare, you look like you must've been kin to some crane out in the swamp! Well, wrap a blanket around you, or somethin', and give me one of them mouse-chawed old buckskins that stingy Squire Godbey foisted on to you instead of proper pay, and I'll fox them pants so they won't tear again! I'll sew a facin' of hide that'll never rip, not even after the pants themselves is wore out complete. You never see a tore-up deer, did you? And they're all the time out in the brush. I'll do the same with your jacket, too."

While Hannah was busy that evening, stitching through the heavy deerskin and laying on a neat covering to the torn places which she had patched from below, Abraham played with the children and told them stories. After a rousing rough-and-tumble which made the cabin shake, he finally put the children to bed and then had a long discussion with Jack Armstrong about Andy Jackson's latest misdeeds in Washington City. Hannah, frowning with eyestrain in the meager candlelight, sewed on and on.

"Them pants legs must be all of five feet long, I do declare," she cried wearily, finishing at last. "There, now you look like a real surveyor and won't all the time be so ragged. Now hand over them socks you got on—I declare to heaven, a pure disgrace! What do you do to your socks, Abe? Just see them holes, and I only mended them last week. Must've been et by rats!"

98

CHAPTER ELEVEN

The reverend peter cartwright arrived with a roar, expounded with thunder and departed as with a hurricane. No spot was ever quite the same after this smoke-breathing Methodist circuit rider came around, nor was anyone quite so comfortable, nor so self-assured, when he had gone. His words were seldom calm or quiet. He seemed quite unable to talk in anything less than a bellow laced with strong words highly flavored with fire, brimstone and eternal punishment. He could sway an audience of five thousand people so that they wept, groaned, tore their hair, groveled on the ground, lay rigid in fear, or went into crying spells, hysterics or heart attacks.

It was Peter Cartwright's peculiar privilege to exhort the people of Sangamon County to foreswear sin and enter into the protective arms of the Lord. Consequently, he was the damper on many a dance, the reproving eye at drinking establishments. He took the joy out of life, some said. There were those, however, who felt they were indeed saved from the fiery pit. After a camp meeting, they went about with a transcendent sort of light around them, which gradually wore off as the prairie preacher's words grew somewhat dimmed by time, space and temptation. Nevertheless, the Sangamon country's farthest reaches and some beyond were purged and purified by his earnest, earthy, furious ministrations.

Peter Cartwright on his fat bay horse blew into New Salem one mild, muddy day in March to dicker for a few items at Sam

Hill's store. He and Sam cordially disliked each other. When the two were in the store together, Abraham Lincoln, often the innocent bystander, could almost see the sparks fly and smell the brimstone.

"Brother Hill," Cartwright began carefully, after he had made his purchases. He spoke gently enough, his tousled mop of black curls tossed every which way as he pulled off his big, dirty white, broad-brimmed hat. "Have you gotten anywhere in repenting your sins since I was in here last?" He scowled questioningly under his shaggy brows at Sam Hill's strong-featured face.

Sam spoke briefly, holding himself in check and waiting on another customer at the same time. Besides, Peter had just bought two dollars' worth of merchandise and he didn't like to insult a customer who paid cash.

"Reckon I've got about as far at repentin' as you've got at convertin' me to be a shoutin' Methodist, Uncle Peter."

"I'm not your Uncle Peter, nor any kin, thank fortune," exploded Cartwright. "If I was, I'd likely feel more down in the mouth than I do about your sad lack of grace and your impending doom. You know what's likely to happen to you, Samuel, when you go to meet your Maker?"

"No, I don't, and I doubt if you do, either, Uncle Pete."

"Don't call me Uncle, and don't call me Pete! If you can't be civil, shut up!" snapped Cartwright, beginning to seethe. "*I* know what will happen. The Lord'll take one whiff of that odor of sin a-risin' from your ornery carcass, and He'll send you on down to keep company with one who's less squeamish and who's more in your category. Lucifer's just a-waitin' and eager for such as you, Samuel Hill!"

He was set off now and going to be hard to stop. People passing by the store paused to see what the racket was about. Peter Cartwright could always draw a crowd, wherever he was. Sam Hill, realizing this, let the preacher rant. It was good for business to keep him going for a while, although there were limits to what Sam could stand.

"Down below there where there's no escape, he'll dangle you

over them eternal beds of fiery coals, and there you'll be, scorched and singed, screamin' for mercy and wishin' you'd have another chance, but no, it'll be too late. You got to take your salvation now and repent, brother, repent!"

"I ain't no brother of yours," retorted Sam furiously, keeping a canny eye on the customers and detecting none who had come to buy, only to listen, "and when I want to repent of what few sins I figure I've committed in this life, I can do it without you standin' by to hold my hand. Now I'll thank you to take your purchases and git!"

Peter Cartwright, smiling sadly and patiently at Sam Hill's angry face and looking around at the men who were grinning at the scene, and at the women who were trying not to show their own enjoyment, took up his parcels and walked out. He only went as far as the porch, however. There he sat down on the edge, his short legs dangling, and began to heckle Sam. The latter could hear him all too plainly from inside the store.

"Poor Sam!" Cartwright sighed gustily, carefully replacing his big white hat on his head. "I feel mighty sorry for that poor sinner, bound for perdition at the rate he's a-goin'. He's not content to head for hell under his own power, he's darin' the Almighty to help him out with a boost in the right direction. Ain't that so, Sam?" he called, raising his voice so that Sam could hear, though that individual had no trouble in understanding everything uttered in Cartwright's usually stentorious tones. Neither had Dr. Allen across the street nor Dr. Regnier next door.

"Shut your trap, Cartwright!" yelled Sam. "You'll wake the dead!"

"If I do, it's for their own good, and yours, too. They'll tell you I'm right. Yes, it's a pity," went on the preacher in more normal tones, elaborately tinged with sadness. "I used to think there wasn't no hope at all for that poor sinner inside there, name of Sam Hill, because I felt sure he didn't even have a soul, so far gone in evil ways he was.

"But one day I discovered that he did have a soul. Do you gentlemen know how I found that out?"

"How, Peter?" the bystanders asked, grinning.

"Well, I'll tell you," he began softly, then letting his voice gain volume by inches to the climax. "One day when I was doin' business in there with this poor sinner, Mr. Hill, I slyly held up a quarter of a dollar to his mouth. And what do you think, that so-called soul of his came a-guggling up his windpipe—glug-glug-glug—to snatch that there coin before I could take it away! Yes, gentlemen, Samuel Hill does have a soul—a mighty mean, tarnished, green-scummed, money-hungry soul."

Inside the store, Abraham thought his business associate would explode.

"Now, I've had my doubts about some of you other sinners," went on Cartwright, determinedly looking with accusation about him. "Either your soul is mighty puny and starved, like a deer after a hard winter, or you feed it on poison and that's the surest way to kill your immortal soul and head you on the road to perdition that I know of.

"Now you take that Lincoln in there. Associatin' with Sam Hill like he does, you'd expect him to have caught Sam's money disease, and have a scrawny, corroded soul, but he ain't got that, not with the way that feller can't hold on to a dollar. But look how he dares Providence with them books he reads!"

"What books you mean, Mr. Cartwright?" piped up young Tom Onstot.

"Them free-thought books, that's what, sonny!" snapped Cartwright, bending a severe look upon the boy. "Especially that horrid work of the devil, called *The Age of Reason*, or some such nonsensical title, by that condemned atheist, Tom Paine. If that ain't the work of Satan himself, I'm not Peter Cartwright!"

"Now hold on, Cartwright," said Abraham Lincoln quietly. Detaching himself from the postmaster's tall stool and emerging onto the porch, he stood tall above the short, furious, prairie preacher. "Aren't you assuming a lot just on the strength of your own opinions? How can you be so sure you're the one that's right and nobody else? You got a special communication from the Lord Himself?"

Peter Cartwright for a moment was speechless, but only for a moment. It was not often that anyone questioned what he said.

"Blasphemy!" he roared, banging his fist on the porch so that the mud-clots jumped. "Downright blasphemy! 'Have I got a special communication from the Lord!' he asks."

"Well, how can you be sure?" pursued Lincoln, thinking his way along without getting ruffled, while Cartwright was boiling. "And why can't someone else's beliefs be just as likely to find favor above? Seems to me, with all the people and all the beliefs in the world, those that think like you do, Peter Cartwright, are sort of few. Does that mean all the rest of us are bound for perdition? What about our founding fathers who proclaimed freedom of worship in America? They didn't specify Baptists or Methodists or Presbyterians or Catholics, just freedom to worship God."

"Abe Lincoln," began the Reverend Cartwright, holding himself in check with a tremendous effort. "You—mark—my—words! You're goin' to be the first to go and one of those to stay down there the longest. The world ain't the same as it used to be, when men trembled in fear of the Lord and didn't dast question holy writ!"

"I'd just as soon tremble in fear of my own sins and respect the Lord for having the good judgment to understand human nature and not knock me down for *being* human," said Lincoln soberly. "You keep on with what you believe, Reverend, and I'll keep on believing what I've thrashed out for myself over many a long and wakeful night and day, and I reckon we'll both do all right. You going, Peter? Give my kind regards to Mrs. Cartwright."

Peter Cartwright, with his big white hat clamped down tight and low on his furrowed brow and his broad face dark with a fury which he somehow couldn't find words to spit forth, got aboard his fat horse and gouged his heels violently into its well-padded ribs. Someone handed him his purchases, and the beast started off at a startled jog trot which slowed to a walk before the steed had reached the outskirts of New Salem and headed southwest toward the Cartwright home.

"Well, I'll be hog-tied and hamstrung, if that ain't the first time I ever see old Uncle Peter without ary word to say!" exploded one of the loungers on the porch.

"Never thought I'd live to see the day, and him the shoutin'est preacher in Illinois! He actually was speechless; and when Peter Cartwright can't think of a word to say to put down a upstart like Abe Lincoln and his fool idees, the end of the world is sure enough at hand!"

"Land, did you see his face? It was red as a turkey's feet in pokeberry time! If he don't act more calm and collected, he's goin' to bust a blood vessel."

"Lincoln was right about that freedom of worship, though," said another man thoughtfully. "Likely that's what corked up the Reverend thataway. He'd naught to come back with on a subject like that!"

"I'm sorry I made him mad," said Abraham regretfully, thinking back on the distasteful incident. "But after all, it's not his business how I think, what I think, what I read or what I believe! I figure it's a touchy business to question and pry and dig into a man's private religion, then rant and rail at him for holding to what he believes."

"You're right there, Lincoln," asserted Sam Hill, who still burned from the heckling administered by Cartwright. "He needed to be taken down a peg!"

"I'm sorry I sent him off like that, though," added Abraham. "It sure doesn't seem quite right for old Peter to go so quietly. You think he was sick?"

"Quiet?" exploded Nelson Alley. "That feller was about as quiet as a tornado comin' acrost the prairie, only it was all pent up inside of him. Wait till he runs afoul of some sinner on the road towards home, and I bet he busts out all over the countryside, preachin' his fire and brimstone again till you can hear him clear to Athens!"

CHAPTER TWELVE

Iɴ ᴛʜᴇ sᴘʀɪɴɢ of 1834, Abraham Lincoln made his plans to run again as candidate for the State Legislature. His 1832 defeat was somewhat dimmed by time; the hurt was not so great, the blow to his confidence eased. He felt that he had grown up a good deal since that other campaign. Perhaps this time things would be different.

To his astonishment, both Democrats and Whigs backed him. To Lincoln, this did not seem quite honest; it was not legal, or something. However, after consultation with John Todd Stuart, who assured him that he was not only honest but lucky, he accepted the partial aid of the opposition with a thankful, if puzzled, heart.

It had all come about oddly enough, he thought. Judge Bowling Green had started it.

"Abe, son, if you're going to win that election, you're going to have to convert some of the Democrats to your side. There aren't enough Whigs in Sangamon County to swing it," the portly squire warned, folding his plump hands over his large and protruding front expansion.

"Well, how?" asked Abraham, willing to listen and learn.

"I, for one, as a Democrat, will do my best," promised the magistrate. "Plenty of 'milk-and-cider' Democrats in the bushes; they're easy enough to bring over to your side if you butter up to them right. Even some of the 'whole-hog' Jackson men might be persuaded . . ."

So, as Squire Green was electioneering, "beating the bushes," as he put it, to roust out the undecided Democrats to vote Whig, a party of Democrats came to see Lincoln.

"Sir, we propose to eliminate two of our weaker Democratic candidates, leaving only the Honorable Richard Quinton, and come to your support. We feel you are more worthy than the men on our side, all but Mr. Quinton, sir."

"Well, now, that's mighty handsome of you gentlemen," said Lincoln cautiously, dazzled but somewhat confused and wary at this friendliness from the enemy.

"That is," they continued blandly, "if you will help us squeeze out John Stuart in the race for the Legislature."

There it was, the possum in the hayrick, the sandbur under the saddle. They wanted something in return for their favors. Which was only natural among politicians, Abraham figured. He looked noncommittal, an art he had perfected to some degree of skill. His bony face expressed nothing.

"I'll have to give it some thought, gentlemen. I'll let you know."

"Don't think too long, Lincoln," they warned, somewhat disgruntled that he had not at once leaped to their offer. "We might get tired waiting and change our minds!"

Abraham lost little time in riding over to Springfield. John Todd Stuart was in his office.

"Stuart, they're out to get you! They want me to help crowd you out! If this is politics—then I'm through with it!"

John Todd Stuart smiled and laid a calming hand on Lincoln's agitated shoulder.

"Yes, that's politics, Lincoln. But you stay with it. Now I'll tell you what to do—"

After the conference, Abraham Lincoln, feeling exhilarated with the spirit of battle, rode back to New Salem.

He was to dicker with the Democrats, string along with them, while Stuart, with infinite strategy, directed the Whig campaign against that single fighting Democrat, Mr. Quinton.

It was a good fight and a hot one. And on election day, it was Abraham Lincoln who won by an overwhelming vote—at least it overwhelmed him. He polled second to the largest number of votes for the four candidates elected. John Stuart had had more trouble than he had expected in beating Richard Quinton, and had only managed to get in by the narrowest of margins.

Lincoln, however, had won so easily that he could scarcely credit his good fortune, and his gratitude for the kindness of his fellow men made him glow. One day he was just a poor surveyor, postmaster, store clerk, lying on the ground with his feet propped against a tree, while the ants crawled up his pants leg, as he studied a law book loaned him by John Stuart.

The next day he was in politics, elected as a lawmaker for the august State of Illinois, an honorable legislator, representative from the largest county in the state. He—the Honorable Abraham Lincoln of New Salem, no less!

And one day he was an object of contempt as Squire Godbey, seeing him evidently wasting valuable time, had asked what he was doing, if anything.

"Why, I'm studying law, Squire," he had said placidly, not looking up.

"Law! My good heavenly day! *Law!*" And in disgust, Godbey had departed.

Next day, though, it was:

"How-do, Mr. Lincoln, congratulations, sir!"

Oh, it made a difference, a big and lovely difference. All of a sudden he, Abraham Lincoln, was someone. It was all very heady and pleasant. It scared him, too. All he had to do now was to live up to the confidence people had placed in him, and, after all, what did he know about being a legislator!

In order to learn to do so with some measure of skill, he took John Stuart's suggestion.

"I'd go in for the law, if I were you, Lincoln," the handsome young Springfield lawyer, only two years older than Lincoln, had said one day when Abraham was deploring his lack of knowledge to equip him to be a lawmaker.

"The principles of justice and truth which you'll learn in that profession will help you in the Legislature, and you'll have a profitable career during the remainder of the year and all the rest of your life. You've already some background in law. You say you got a smattering of it back in Indiana and in New Salem, too. I hear you've been making out papers and forms and deeds for people, and that certainly takes some knowledge of law!"

"Well, I do just a little. I don't charge for my services though. Just chalk 'em up to experience."

"You come over to my office and borrow all the books you need; I'll suggest certain ones you'll get the most from. You go into law, Lincoln, and if you're as good at it as I think you will be, you can come in as my partner when Dummer leaves."

Well, that honor alone was incentive enough. Abe lived, ate, drank and thought little else but law, just as he had lived, eaten, drunk and thought higher mathematics and surveying when he had needed to learn them. There was nothing halfway about him when he wanted to absorb something.

For a while, however, it seemed that he would need all his knowledge of law to get himself out of his own financial difficulties. Those debts of his were suddenly coming to howl like a hungry prairie wolf on his doorstep.

One sweet, fair day, back in April, 1834, when it would seem that surely nothing unpleasant could ever happen again in such a blossoming, greening, singing, fragrant world, the preliminary blow had fallen. Reuben Radford had assigned to one Peter Van Bergen of Springfield a part interest in the Lincoln-Berry note, for the balance of the sum owing on the contents of the store which they had bought from Radford and Billy Greene. Peter Van Bergen, a testy Teuton, a deputy land agent and speculator in real estate, had no patience with waiting around for his money. Mr. Van Bergen, therefore, brought suit for immediate payment.

If there was anything in the world which was impossible for Abraham Lincoln and William Berry, it was immediate payment on anything.

The sum was $204.82. Since William Greene was the original signer of the note, long ago on that bitter January day when the Clary's Grove boys had wrecked Reuben Radford's store, it was he alone, at first, who was sued. Greene was considerably irked to be charged with a note in which he now had no part. So he in turn sued his friends, Lincoln and Berry.

Nothing more came of it, then, except to transfer responsibility of the debt until October. This was presumably considered to be time enough for the former partners to raise the required cash. However, the store was growing steadily less prosperous for William Berry, who was ill and who still drank too much. Lincoln hadn't earned much with his surveying and his postmaster's job. The time finally arrived in the autumn when the issue could no longer be evaded.

In desperation, the two consulted.

"We just haven't enough money between us to pay," mourned Abraham Lincoln, staring at Bill's floor which badly needed sweeping. "And we have even fewer assets. I don't know what to do next. It's like pounding sand down a rat hole to try and pay our debt off in the dribbles we have."

"I think I'll have a drink," said Bill Berry, his hand trembling violently as he poured out a glassful for himself.

"Well, there's my horse," he went on gloomily. A fit of coughing doubled him over in pain and stopped what he was saying.

"Yes, your horse, and mine, too," added Lincoln, "though mine isn't paid for, and I guess it can't be turned in legally. I reckon Tom Watkins'll be down on me like a duck on a June bug for his own money pretty soon, when he hears the others are gathering around with their hands out. Bill," he added pityingly, "you ought to do something for that cough of yours. It sounds bad. Worse than it did. Did you see Doctor Allen?"

"Yes, and Doc Regnier, and Doctor Henry in Springfield. They can't help me. Nobody can," added Bill somberly. "Nothing except what I'm drinking, for a little while, anyway."

William Berry did not look at Abraham, but kept his shaking hands clutched around his glass. Abraham noted that Bill was growing thinner and his eye-sockets looked dark and hollow, his face without color.

"There's nothing for you to do but sell out, I reckon," Lincoln said, going back to the other subject. "You haven't much left, I guess. As for me, I reckon about all I own personally is my surveying instruments. They might bring in a little cash."

"Oh, no, Lincoln, you can't do that!" cried his former partner, aghast. "You won't have any way to make a living without those instruments!" Bill looked shocked.

"Can't be helped," Abraham replied grimly. "I'm not one to live in luxury when my creditors are crying for their just dues."

When the sale took place, enough was realized to satisfy Van Bergen. Berry had sold his horse for additional cash. Billy Greene donated one of his toward raising more money.

And Abraham Lincoln, with despair in his soul, had seen his surveying instruments lying on the counter, waiting for a buyer. He couldn't bear to watch any longer. He went out into the cool, bright, lovely autumn morning.

Skeins of snow geese were patterning their long streamers over New Salem. He watched them flash white with black wing-tips in a wavy sort of flight, high and serene and untroubled, against a cobalt sky, until they were beyond the crimson and orange maples on the hills to the south. The fairy tinkling of distant goose voices came down like bells to him.

He took a brief walk in the glowing woods and felt more calm. When he went back into the store, the sale was over, the people gone. The compass, grapevine chain and saddlebags, however, still lay on the dusty, splintery counter. Probably nobody had wanted them.

Kindly James Short, as always neatly turned out and precise, stepped into the store. He smiled at Abraham's troubled, unhappy face.

"Here they are, Abe," he said, moving forward to lay his hand on the compass. "I thought you'd never come. I bid them in. They're all yours again."

"Jimmy!" Abraham caught the little man's firm hands, then

almost hugged him. "I'll pay you back if it's the last thing I ever do!"

"No hurry, Lincoln. No hurry. It was a pleasure to do it. Couldn't let you lose those things, especially since I've got a job of surveying coming up myself soon, and I'll need the best surveyor in Sangamon County to do it for me!"

But other creditors, like buzzards, caught the smell of payments in the air and gathered around for their share, alarmed lest the meager funds be exhausted before they had a chance.

Tom Watkins was one of these.

"He ain't never paid me for that there horse I give him. A mighty good mare and a good saddle and bridle, too, by gum. I aim to get me my money whilst he's still got some. I ain't goin' to see that nag of mine go to pay someone else's account and from what I been hearin', them two is turnin' in everything they got."

Tom Watkins thereupon hastily sued Lincoln in New Salem, to get ahead of the slower courts of law in Springfield. Somehow, though, Abraham Lincoln scraped up the $57.50 he owed Watkins.

And there he was, stripped. Abraham Lincoln stood literally penniless, with only the clothes on his back, a few battered books and his surveying instruments and old horse his sole possessions in life. It was October, 1834.

Things certainly would have to improve before November. At that time, he would be going to Vandalia as a legislator, and he would have to appear in something other than what he stood in after he'd paid his debts. He would need decent clothes; also transportation, unless he walked all the way; board and room, too, if he cared to eat and sleep while there. Besides, he knew that a certain dignity was owing to the position to which he had been elected.

"Well, Lincoln," said Coleman Smoot one day, when Abraham told him some of his difficulties. "I voted for you in August, so I reckon I can take on the responsibility and honor of seein' that you look decent to assume the job. I got some extra cash I ain't needin' for a while. I'll loan it out to you, and you can pay me when you get your money from your work in Vandalia."

"Smoot, that's right handsome of you!" exclaimed Lincoln, beaming. "I don't know what I'd do without my friends in New Salem. Here, I'll sign a note and you'll have your money next spring when I get back."

Coleman Smoot loaned him two hundred dollars. It seemed to Lincoln that he no sooner got out of one debt before he was up to his neck in another, but at least he had some real money looming in the offing. Legislators were paid three dollars a day, plus the cost of their transportation. A three-months' term in the Legislature would amount to a good deal, he figured.

CHAPTER THIRTEEN

On a foggy November day in 1834, the rattling stagecoach from Springfield rolled and jounced over the ruts of the long and tiresome road south to Vandalia, Illinois. The horses' hoofs thudded on heavy clods, not yet frozen hard, the wheels groaned through mud holes. The creaking coach rolled from side to side, throwing its occupants against each other and sending their luggage, lodged on the roof, skidding against the retaining rack and back again. Inside the coach were two senators and four legislators. Of the six, John Todd Stuart and Abraham Lincoln were tallest.

The two talked absorbedly, meanwhile holding on to the straps to keep from going in a heap when the coach lurched. Stuart was elegant, noble of bearing and said to be the handsomest man in Illinois. He was a knowing and seasoned legislator and politician. His companion, Lincoln, was not so well dressed, certainly not so handsome nor so confident. He was thankful that Stuart had taken him on as his protégé and would show him how to act and get around in Vandalia and the capitol building's august halls. It was certainly all a new and strange world to the man from New Salem who, a drifter and day laborer, had arrived in a cottonwood canoe three years earlier. He might not be any richer than he was then, but he knew he was different, better educated, better equipped in his mind to meet the challenges which lay ahead.

"Yes, Vandalia's been the state capital since 1819, a year after Illinois became a state," Stuart was saying on the second day, as the smoking chimneys of the capital loomed far ahead. "Kaskaskia had it first because it was the old French territorial capital since 1700, but it wouldn't do for long. The Mississippi evidently was bent on eating it up and depositing the capital in the water!"

Lincoln laughed. He knew that old river and what it could do.

"I never did know why they chose the place they did, though," Lincoln said. "Of all the places in Illinois, why Vandalia?"

"Well, they wanted to move the capital inland and farther north, trying to keep up with the trend of population. Still, they didn't want to get away from contact with the Mississippi, so they chose a bluff-top above the Kaskaskia River. When it was navigable, which wasn't too often, it turned out, you could take a boat below the town and go down to the Mississippi and then up to St. Louis or down to New Orleans. Besides, Vandalia is situated where the National Road is coming through from Washington City to the Mississippi, and that's important, too."

"Why the name?"

"Vandalia? Who knows?" John Stuart's handsome face broke into a laugh. "Likely somebody's wife fancied the name and they used it because she insisted!"

"You mean it wasn't a town before it was the capital?" Lincoln asked slowly. He realized he had somehow neglected a point in the history of his adopted state.

"No, they built a new town to be the capital. It wasn't much at first, just a cluster of log cabins and a far from impressive capitol building. Wait till you see it!"

"What do you mean?"

"That State House is a firetrap and a hazard to life and limb, wouldn't you agree, gentlemen?" queried Stuart, turning for confirmation to the other legislators in the coach, who nodded solemnly.

"Yes, I look for it to fall in on us some time when we've got an especially noisy speaker shouting his points!" replied William Carpenter. "Every now and then, in fact, plaster breaks loose and showers down. The stairs creak alarmingly, and how those upper floors hold the men and benches of the Senate chambers I do not see!"

"Those brick walls actually bulge in places," added John Dawson. "I hear they've had to be propped up again. It's a disgrace to Illinois and the nation to have a State House like that!"

"They say they've improved it since last term by opening the first floor more," said Stuart, "but they may have weakened it by taking out the supporting walls. I don't know. I only know that we are going to have to do something about it this session or next, before there's a calamity and we're all buried alive in a general collapse!"

John Stuart laughed, but he was serious about the matter and so were the others. Something would have to be done, and soon.

"What we really need," Stuart added, "is to move the capital to another place more centrally located. Vandalia was only to have it for twenty years, anyway, with an option to continue for another twenty, if it remained at the center of population."

The stage driver gave his tired horses a cut with the whip and bowled in high style into Vandalia's main street.

Stuart and Lincoln took a room at the Vandalia Inn, which was about as comfortable, Stuart said, as any in that tavern-filled town. Already, many of the representatives and senators, as well as members of the supreme court had arrived. Many had brought their wives, and these had come with great trunks and bulging portmanteaux containing their best finery to impress the other lawmakers' wives at the winter's social affairs.

"The ladies try to make Vandalia's social season as gay and fine as any in New Orleans or Nashville, but I'm afraid Vandalia will never be able to compete with those centers of culture and delight! Still, the ladies, God bless 'em, have done a lot to make the General Assembly bearable, and if you stumble over their trunks in the hall—as now—" added Stuart, stepping high over a heap of luggage which just had been deposited in the dark hall of the inn, "you just smile and are glad that such things have come to the frontier. In fact, you can hardly call us a frontier nowadays, Lincoln. And did I tell you that you look mighty spruce yourself?"

Abraham Lincoln in some pride agreed that he did look mighty spruce. He had on his first suit of tailor-made clothes, and the glory of his attire, topped with a tall silk hat, caused him now and again to look down his imposing black length with considerable awe and wonderment that this should be he. He had always worn coarse butternut jeans, homespuns, linsey pants, and tow-linen stuff that pricked and shrunk. He might start out with pants and coat which came decently down his bony wrists and long legs to his shoe tops, but in a little while, somehow, they always looked high-water and fit him all wrong. Not that he minded. How he appeared seldom bothered him. Ugly as he was, what was the use in dressing fancy? But when he was elected to the Legislature, he didn't need John Todd Stuart, in his elegant broadcloth, stock and silk hat, to tell him that he'd have to get something a trifle better to wear.

With the funds borrowed from Coleman Smoot, he went to Springfield and to a tailor whom Stuart recommended, where Lincoln was carefully measured and his broad-shouldered frame fitted as well as the somewhat perplexed tailor could manage. Abraham Lincoln paid out sixty dollars, ultimately, for the finished suit.

He felt a bit uncomfortable, if elegant, in Vandalia, with his fine black, tight-fitting, long-enough trousers and flowered waistcoat, and the long black coat flaring below his hips. A high black stock was wound around and around his neck to hold his white collar fashionably high and flared, though it worried him, forever poking him in the cheek or rasping his ears. He wished he could look as easy and fine as Stuart did, but then, Stuart had been brought up in a life of elegance in Kentucky and had known how to dress from the beginning. No doubt, Abe figured with an inner grin, John Stuart had been elegant in his cradle!

Lincoln and Stuart went downstairs to join the others. The main room of the Vandalia Inn was seething with men, smoke and talk. Abraham Lincoln, who liked people, loved the sound and the look of the place, yet he was thankful he had Stuart to introduce him, to get started knowing a few people, just as an entering wedge. From then on, he'd be mostly on his own, but he could handle that. He had always found it easy to make friends.

The two tall men from Sangamon moved in on a group sitting around a scarred deal table where they were finishing supper.

"Ah, how do you do, gentlemen?" put in courtly John Stuart, laying his hand affectionately on the shoulder of one of the seated men. "Now that the delegation from Sangamon has arrived, let the proceedings begin!"

"Stuart! Welcome back! Here, pull up a chair and join us," cried Ninian Edwards. "The girl hasn't brought the pudding yet, and if it isn't any better than the rest of the meal, no one will object if she never brings it! No doubt it's the best Vandalia can offer, however. Have you dined, Stuart?"

John Stuart shook his head. "Gentlemen," he said in his cultured, compelling, well modulated voice which never had to shout for attention. "Gentlemen, I here present to you our new member from Sangamon, my good friend and constituent, Abraham Lincoln."

Abraham's big hand shot out to shake the hands of the men around the table, who rose to greet him. They were appraising him with experienced eyes. A raw, crude young man, no style, no proper manners and likely few brains, he felt they were thinking.

Ninian Wirt Edwards, son of the territorial governor of Illinois, seeking election as attorney-general, rose and bowed over Lincoln's big paw.

"Charmed, Mr. Lincoln," said Mr. Edwards smoothly, his own lily-white palm feeling the callouses on the New Salem hand gripping his with a confoundedly firm clasp. "Welcome to our select throng!"

"And this is Orville Browning of Quincy, who is also a Whig and my good friend, Lincoln," went on Stuart, "and beside him, as you know, is John Dawson who rode down here with us, and Mr. Carpenter, and this gentleman sitting beside Mr. Dawson is General William Lee Davidson Ewing, our acting governor. General Ewing, Mr. Lincoln of Sangamon."

The general bowed. He eyed Lincoln peculiarly as he sat down again, murmuring polite amenities. Abraham also eyed General

117

Ewing with some inward alarm. No wonder the acting governor looked so oddly at him! Abraham Lincoln remembered with some trepidation a certain hot Fourth of July in 1830. It was back in Decatur, when Mr. Posey and General Ewing were Independence Day speakers who were campaigning for themselves at the same time.

He remembered their not too brilliant speeches and how the frontier crowd had been irked because the two had either forgotten or had chosen to ignore the custom of the politician's treating the crowd to drinks. He recalled how the crowd had then hailed him, Abraham Lincoln, young and gawky and ignorant, not long in Illinois from Indiana, and had gotten him up on a stump to talk, too.

He was only twenty-one at the time, and he burned now as he recalled how pompous he must have sounded, airing his valued opinions about river improvements and navigation of the Sangamon as if he were an authority, and how the applause for him had been embarrassingly greater, somehow, than for the estimable Mr. Posey and General Ewing.

Maybe the general didn't remember. Lincoln fervently hoped he did not and never would connect this self-consciously dignified Sangamon County representative in his first tailor-made suit with the blab-mouthed youth in butternut jeans and no shoes standing on a stump over in Decatur.

The general, whose memory was long, had not forgotten, however.

"I see that you have come up in the world, Mr. Lincoln. My congratulations!" And he smiled a trifle sarcastically as he turned back to the pudding which the frowsy, overworked little servant girl had plumped down in front of him.

"What does General Ewing mean by that, Mr. Lincoln?" asked Ninian Edwards with a smile, applying spoon to pudding. He scented something interesting between the two.

"Well—ah—well, you see—some time ago General Ewing and I were speakers on the same, ah, platform, so to speak. I believe, ah—ahem—I think what he refers to is the fact that, on that auspicious occasion, the general wore shoes and, uh—well, I did not! I had on an old calico shirt and butternut pants that went half-way down my calf and then stopped short—got discouraged with so far to go, no doubt. The general gave a good speech; but I can't say I exactly shone. I am honored tonight to dine at the same table with General Ewing."

With this situation neatly disposed of, the laughter subsiding, Abraham settled down to absently devouring his supper. He discovered that part of the meal consisted of stewed pumpkin, as well as a bowl of fried pumpkin chips, and he was not particularly fond of either of them. He had eaten too much pumpkin in a poverty-stricken lifetime. Pushing away the bowl of pumpkin chips, he said drily:

"This puts me in mind of the preacher up our way who got more than his fill of this noble fruit. This parson had been preach-ing to folk in the Pecan Bottoms, a mighty poor and sandy region down the Sangamon from New Salem. At house after house the women fed him pumpkin—stewed, fried, baked, as pudding, as soup, as pie or as each female had decided to cook it that day. He began to get mighty tired of the stuff."

The men around the table were listening. After Lincoln's adept parrying of General Ewing's snobbishness, they were inter-ested in what he might say next. There was a neat spice to the way this backwoodsman talked.

"Well," Lincoln went on, noting the interest, "one day the preacher was asked to say grace before dinner, and, casting his experienced eye over the table fittings, he commenced his prayer thusly:

" 'And now, Lord, may it please Thee to blast the pumpkin crop, for we cannot perform our work on such a diet!' Which is the way I feel about it, too, I reckon!"

As he finished his supper, Abraham listened intently to the political conversations flowing around him. It was a complicated business, politics, but one of the most fascinating things he had ever listened to or been a part of. Even after his somewhat inauspicious beginning, he could hardly wait to get going.

The talk abruptly died down. Ninian Edwards nudged John Stuart as an extraordinarily short, stout, handsome young man walked pompously and with poise through the crowded room and up the staircase.

"He's here," Edwards sneered. "Let's everyone know it, too."

"Who is he?" asked Lincoln, interested that such a small man should cause such a great one as Ninian Edwards a moment's notice.

"That's Stephen A. Douglas," put in Stuart. "He's the thorn in our flesh, though we rather like the fellow in spite of it. Wants to be state's attorney, and he takes the floor whenever there is half an opening. Douglas's a strong politician, and if a young schoolteacher can rise in the world by spouting his own merits, then I say let him get on with it. How else can you manage? Can't always wait for your friends to pipe up loudly enough to make the right people hear! I predict Douglas will go a long way in spite of his being a Democrat!"

The laughter went around the table; then the conversation turned to other matters, supper was cleared, cigars were smoked, drinks were brought, and hour after hour the men who would meet next day on the Senate or House floors were thrashing out the problems which lay ahead. Lincoln found out that more expert lobbying took place over the tables of Vandalia Inn, the Charter Tavern and other hostelries than actually took place in the drafty, cold, poorly built State House.

John Stuart, still feeling responsible for the new member from Sangamon, went next morning with him up the steps of the capitol building and they entered the large, bare chamber together. It was milling with representatives, all of them dressed in tight trousers and long black coats with broad lapels, some of them of black satin or velvet. Abraham Lincoln, feeling uncomfortable, yet, for once in his life, suitably garbed, was thankful he hadn't been forced to wear his rough frontier clothes.

The House of Representatives was undeniably large and bare. It had no degree of elegance. Members were to sit three to a table, and already were drawing lots for seats. The Speaker of the House sat on a raised platform, but his only other point of distinction was that he had his table to himself and his inkstand was made of pewter, while those of the representatives were made of common cork.

The rest of the room was equally as plain and undistinguished. There were boxes of sand to accommodate those who chewed tobacco. The cold, barnlike space was inadequately heated with a fireplace at one end and a stove at the other. If you sat near either one, Abraham found, you roasted in your tight trousers and fancy coat and high-collared shirt, or, if you sat too far from either source of heat, you froze and wished for a buffalo robe and a foot-warmer.

For dark winter days and night sessions, there were candles to make just enough light to see by, and no more. In a corner was a tin bucket filled with water, with a dipper and three tin cups, to relieve the thirst of the dozens of assembled lawmakers.

"I see we've had some improvement there," spoke up John Stuart with a slight tinge of sarcasm in his voice. "We used to have only *one* tin cup for the lot of us!"

When the Speaker briskly rapped his gavel at ten o'clock that first morning and the invocation was uttered in a spirit of reverence due the occasion, most of the members were in their seats. The session was about to begin. The gabble of talk died down as the preliminary business got underway. Lincoln, with Stuart beside him, paid rapt attention, wondering when the important business of lawmaking should begin. He had planned to observe and learn and to keep his mouth shut until he knew the procedure of things, before chancing the occasion of making an abject fool of himself by piping up too soon.

Despite his careful attention, however, matters at hand seemed appallingly unimportant. A few temporary officials were appointed.

There was a roll call for a new Speaker, which gave James Semple the majority, but Semple was a Jacksonian so Stuart and Lincoln, staunch Whigs, voted for his rival. The latter, although not a true Whig, was nevertheless considered less than a "whole-hog" Jackson man, which was something in his favor, anyway. No Whig was put up; there were only seventeen Clay men on the floor and they felt they were not strong enough as a group to override the heavy Jackson vote.

The strategy, Stuart whispered to Lincoln, was to curry favor with the "milk-and-cider" Democrats, insinuate themselves into the good graces of these milder Jacksonians and perhaps, in the final vote, gain power for coming bills by weaning these men over to the Whig camp. This was meaty stuff, the sort of politics Lincoln had been anticipating, and he loved it.

But instead of anything further ensuing along this enthralling line of attack, some minor officials were selected. The post of doorkeeper required seven separate and tiring ballots before one was chosen for that doubtfully stimulating job. There was a small amount of unimportant business which was perfunctorily attended to, while members sat back, crossed their tightly trousered knees and yawned. Several actually went to sleep. Others speculated as to whether the taverns and inns would serve as many game dinners as they had during the previous session, and if the meals in general would be better or worse.

"Venison and prairie chicken every night like last time," Abraham heard a dignified legislator whisper loudly behind him, "is too much for anyone to endure. Why can't they give us a civilized meal once in a while—roast beef, roast pork, kidney pie, things like that? After all, this isn't the frontier!"

Abraham, in whose present life food was of minor importance, thought this was a trifling comment at a time of so great import. While he was musing on the matter, the sharp rapping of the gavel announced that the meeting had adjourned.

Feeling somehow cheated, Abraham Lincoln got up with John Stuart. He was not sure what he had expected, but this sudden termination of a not impressive first meeting of the Seventh Gen-

PETER CARTWRIGHT ... HIS BROAD FACE DARK WITH FURY ... GOT ABOARD HIS FAT
HORSE AND GOUGED HIS HEELS INTO ITS WELL-PADDED RIBS.

SQUIRE GODBEY, SEEING HIM EVIDENTLY WASTING VALUABLE TIME, HAD ASKED WHAT
HE WAS DOING, IF ANYTHING. "WHY, I'M STUDYING LAW, SQUIRE," ABRAHAM HAD
SAID PLACIDLY.

eral Assembly was a decided letdown.

The remainder of the day and evening, however, was spent at the Vandalia Inn, where he and Stuart joined other legislators in worrying about the various problems about to come up before the House, and in planning the strategy for presentation of certain bills. Abraham Lincoln himself had several minor bills of his own in mind which he had promised the Sangamon people to put through if he possibly could, but he thought he would wait a while to learn the procedure before offering his ideas.

On Thursday, Abraham Lincoln's name was put on a Committee of Public Accounts and Expenditures. It was the tenth committee on a list of eleven, and he felt he was included simply because they had to put him on something. He thought it slightly ironical, though, that he, a man of poverty, with many debts still unpaid, should be put on a financial committee! Hah! If they only knew.

On Friday morning, December 5, after the House had turned down the resolution of a member who wanted the powers of local justices enlarged, Mr. Lincoln of Sangamon cleared his throat, addressed the Speaker, was given the floor, and, with an unpleasant trembling in his knees, he presented his intention to introduce his first bill. He had timed this neatly, he felt, since his bill was calculated to limit the jurisdiction of justices of the peace, as contrasted with the preceding bill enlarging their powers.

By the next week, Abraham was in the thick of it. It was in his blood now, all the manipulation of men and ideas, the long hours at night, the careful timing of presentation of ideas and bills. He introduced his second bill. This was "an act to authorize Samuel Musick to build a toll bridge across Salt Creek in Sangamon County." It was of no great interest or import to the majority of the members of the House of Representatives, but was highly important to one Samuel Musick and to the people of Sangamon County who would use his bridge to get across Salt Creek, whereas they had had to ferry before. By its very state-wide insignificance, he felt, it might get through when the bill came up for voting later on.

During his days of watching and listening, of learning and of evaluating what he watched and heard and learned, Lincoln felt he had discovered a way in which legislation could be speeded up and made more efficient. He had noted that endless amendments to bills after they had been read several times clogged proceedings and often left the ultimately approved bill quite changed from what its originator had intended.

When he had been ten whole days in the State Legislature, therefore, Mr. Lincoln of Sangamon stood up to propose his well-considered revision to the House rules—"that it shall not be in order to offer amendments to any bill, after its third reading."

In an astonishingly thick silence, he sat down. Inwardly glowing, because he felt he had indeed hit upon something which would attract favorable attention to himself as a freshman lawmaker and advance his career notably, he could not see why no one spoke.

Then he was taken aback at the storm of dissent which burst, speedily as a prairie storm, upon him. The tempest very quickly disposed of both his ego and his proposal.

He talked to John Stuart and Orville Browning that night, to find out what was so wrong with his idea. It still seemed admirable to him.

"Well, you see, Lincoln," said Browning kindly, "you just haven't been here during the closing days of the session. It's a madhouse then, getting all the bills to harmonize with actions taken in the Senate. We don't work alone, you know; we have to cooperate with what the Senate is doing, too."

"If amendments were limited," put in Stuart, "and all those bills went through up to their final reading at the end of the session, and if they couldn't have those last-minute changes, they would simply be killed. All that season's work would have been for nothing, not to mention disappointments and wrath both here and in the home counties. I agree, your idea sounds excellent, but it would have had the opposite result, you'd have discovered. That's why they made haste to kill it so fast.

"I declare, I thought old Orlando Ficklin would burst a blood vessel, he was in such a hurry to present his nays," added Stuart with a laugh.

"I don't think that Ficklin exactly likes me," put in Lincoln ruefully, remembering the looks of fury bent upon him by the imposing Mr. Ficklin from Wabash County, and the white heat with which he determinedly killed the proposal—and Lincoln's rising pride besides.

The latter's pride slid still further into the depths when his Justice of the Peace bill was amended and referred to a special committee. His ego began to rise again, however, when the Salt Creek Bridge bill actually passed, though slightly amended, but with Lincoln, Stuart and Carpenter doing the revising. Lincoln would have that piece of work accomplished, at least, if he had nothing else to show for his first session in the House.

Time moved on, day after day, with routine business which bored the legislators to such an extent that they voted to take several afternoons off during December. Suddenly, three days before Christmas, members of the Illinois State Legislature began counting the days remaining before its final adjournment in February. They were all too few. If the members were to accomplish all they had set out to do, and all which the home folks had sent them to do, they had better work harder! Members voted unanimously, therefore, to get to business and start work at nine in the morning.

That first morning, most of the men straggled in around nine, but the turnout was neither outstanding nor very wide awake.

"I vote we adjourn until ten o'clock," someone proposed, yawning, and the motion was hastily carried. The men all dragged out to have coffee so that they could wake up more thoroughly. They readjourned at ten, their usual hour. This procedure held for the next several days, and not very much more work was done than before, if as much.

Lincoln of Sangamon was disturbed by this sluggishness and waste of time. Ten o'clock, even nine o'clock—why it was the middle of the day. He was used to rising at dawn and getting down to work at once.

"Gentlemen," he stood up to suggest. "I propose that we do not observe Christmas as a holiday, but spend the day in catching up on the work in which we are so woefully in arrears. After all, many of us are too far from home to get there for Christmas and back in time for the session next day—"

But his high-pitched, earnest voice was drowned in the thunder of nays and he folded down into his Windsor chair in some embarrassment. He didn't like their vehemence nor the cold light of dislike which he detected on the faces of many of his constituents. They might not all have a chance to get home for Christmas, they were muttering, but by Ned, they weren't going to spend Christmas Day slaving in a drafty old State House, voting on dry, dull bills that oughtn't to become laws anyway! Not on Christmas Day, they weren't!

Christmas in Vandalia was a mixture of Illinois frontier, New England, Kentuckian, French and German celebration, or absence of it, depending upon one's persuasion. The combination contrived to put a gala air upon a day which was dismal, with a freezing drizzle that glazed streets and coated trees till they creaked and groaned with the weight of ice.

Indoors, however, there were plenty of hot toddies and mulled cider and eggnog and other festive drinks. The Vandalia Inn actually managed to produce a noble roast of beef for Christmas dinner. Although the meat was a trifle stringy and tough, it was, nevertheless, beef and not deer, bear, wild turkey or prairie chicken, of which everyone by now was heartily sick. The cook turned out a plum pudding which might have done credit to Old England, and made half a dozen pecan pies which were like something straight from New Orleans.

Afterward, some of the more frivolous guests, gathering around the nucleus of the ladies in their best gowns, played snapdragon—snatching raisins out of a bowl of burning brandy. There were dances and games and other social activities, and then more food, more drinks, more fun.

Abraham Lincoln, to whom Christmas held little meaning, spent the day talking politics to anyone who would listen. He took a long walk by himself, out along the ridge above the unfrozen Kaskaskia River, got his good boots muddy and a cold in his head. He slipped and slid over the ice glaze and came back feeling lonely and miserable and sorry for himself.

People seemed to have such a gay time at Christmas, but he somehow didn't know how to go about it. His own family hadn't believed it was proper to celebrate so holy a day frivolously, nor had there ever been enough money to buy extras to make the day special. Thinking back on it, he'd never really known Christmas in all his life and had not missed it until now. Its jollity fell strangely on his ears. Maybe, after all, in spite of his father's calling it a worldly celebration, there was something good and fine and worthwhile in observing Christmas. If he ever had any children of his own, he would see to it that they grew up with Christmas in their lives. The vow made him feel a little better and he was almost cheerful again.

He felt considerably better next morning, though his cold plagued him, for his toll bridge bill passed the Senate. The other bill, however, seemed doomed to being forever tabled; it lay in indefinite postponement.

This dropped his spirits again with a dull thud. Was he sentenced forever to being postponed and put off and held back when his ideas were basically good? He moped around and blew his nose and coughed a lot, and finally had the cold whipped, along with his gloom.

Suddenly, in the closing five weeks of the session, Lincoln found himself serving on no less than ten special committees. He was called upon to present vital motions. Very happily, the House of Representatives found itself enjoying a chance to listen to the often pungently expressed words of Lincoln of Sangamon, and of being fascinated by the charm underlying his unpolished exterior and the ungraceful motions of his hands and feet. His magnetic personality seemed to radiate like an unseen but potent force, drawing men to him and him to them. He did not understand it himself, and neither did his companions, but they felt it. They liked him; he liked them, and they were brought together strangely and compellingly. Even testy Orlando Ficklin had to admit that the young man had something, even if he couldn't very often agree with his notions.

At last it was all over. The gritty floor was swept, the tobacco-clogged sandboxes emptied, the marred tables cleaned, the legislators, one by one, taking the stages or their own horses to their separate destinations. It was February 13, 1835. Governor Duncan went home to Jacksonville, and Lincoln, Stuart, Carpenter and Dawson went back to Springfield. Lincoln had earned $258, plus thirty-three dollars travel expenses, more than enough to pay his full debt to Coleman Smoot and leave a little to live on until surveying jobs came his way again.

New Salem seemed very quiet and dull and lifeless on that winter-spring day, after all the excitement in Vandalia where six hundred people lived. It was difficult for Abraham, at first, to settle down to the slow trend of life and the minor affairs of the village.

Besides, after his absence, he could see a startling thing. New Salem was dying. People were moving away, instead of coming in. No new houses were being built. A curious air of discouragement and stagnation seemed to hang over the village.

And, preceding the death of a village, his friend and one-time partner, William Berry, had died a little more than a month before and had been buried in Rock Creek churchyard. Abraham Lincoln found it a somber homecoming.

CHAPTER FOURTEEN

SAMUEL HILL, in an effort to revive the waning trade of the town and turn a few more profits his way, commenced construction of a carding mill in April. He hired workmen from Petersburg and New Salem, among them the strong-armed Lincoln, to build the biggest structure in New Salem. The complicated machines which were housed in the great rectangular building were brought by boat and ox-cart from New England. They were the marvel of the neighborhood. It was seldom that anyone thereabouts had a chance to see a machine like that.

Sam Hill advertised that he would begin carding wool on May 1st, 1835, and promised an excellent piece of work. People came on horseback, in wagons or on foot, with wool done up in sacks and old petticoats fastened up with locust thorns, until the wool house was full. The machine thumped and growled all day as the ox tethered on the turntable behind the big building supplied the power which made the great wooden cogs revolve and turn the million-bristled cylinders. Through these, the dirty, tangled wool passed and came out straight and free from foreign matter, ready to be spun into yarn on spinning wheels of New Salem and round about.

That spring and summer, Sam was making money. Nearly everyone else in New Salem, however, was losing money, or barely staying solvent, but not the enterprising Sam. He turned some of his profits into the building of a two-story house beside the store, and in July he asked the stately Parthena Nance to marry him. To no one's surprise, she accepted him, and they were married in the biggest and most elaborate wedding ceremony the village had ever seen.

Abraham Lincoln, meanwhile, was spending as much time as he could in studying law and taking jobs of surveying and other work whenever they turned up. When he could, he rode out to Sandridge to visit the Rutledges. He had missed them more than he had at first realized and felt as if he were going home when he paid a call. Mrs. Rutledge invariably asked him to stay to dinner, and he would spend long hours talking with Mr. Rutledge and with David and Robert, who were home from college and had plenty to discuss.

The Rutledges were almost like his own family, Abraham would think happily, after a long session of talk, or a conversation with pretty, red-haired Ann about what they had both been reading. Ann was making plans for going to college and had been working at the Shorts' to help earn money to pay her way.

Ann was such a nice girl. It was a shame, he often thought, how her fiance, John McNeil—which wasn't even his right name, all New Salem had discovered—had never come back to marry her. There was something shady there, but no one knew exactly what it was.

Sam Hill had proposed to Ann, but had been turned down, for she still felt bound to the man who had evidently stepped out of her life. He had not been heard from in several years.

Abraham was fond of Ann, but he had been almost shocked when Sam Hill jokingly had asked if he was going to marry her— he, Abraham Lincoln, with no money, no proper job, no prospects! The very thought of marriage frightened him. Besides, Ann seemed almost like a sister. Just about everyone loved little Annie Rutledge, he figured, felt sorry about her disappointments and applauded her plans for more education. But marriage—!

During the great heat of early August, both Ann and her father fell desperately ill. Abraham hastened out to Sandridge, to see if there was anything he could do, but there was nothing. Both patients were delirious and did not know him. It was very hot. He wished it would rain. The ill turned and moaned on their hot beds and could not ease their pain and discomfort in the sticky, humid atmosphere.

All day long on August 17 there was an odd, steely glare in the sky, with a curious, uncomfortable, ominous feeling in the close air. Everyone seemed to sense it, but no one knew what it meant. It made women snap at their husbands and slap their children; it made dogs, overcome with the heat, resent any overture from man or beast. Horses kicked and flies settled persistently on everyone and everything, and bit and bit and bit.

The water in the Sangamon was very low, too slow to run the mill. It just lay sluggish and unpleasantly stagnant, fetid in the heat. Catfish, flopping miserably in the shallows where they were stranded, slowly died. Herons poked along the algae-greened mud and picked at clam shells which gaped odorously in the heat. Duckweed coating the backwaters gave off its own sickening smell. Grasshoppers shrilled in the dusty horseweeds or chewed the rolled corn leaves, out in the baking fields.

Night was scarcely more comfortable than day. The sun set in a curious, ruddy haze and vanished abruptly as a dark cloud rose levelly out of the west. A wind got up which was thick with dust.

Abraham Lincoln was reading by the light of a candle which was attracting all the small night moths of the neighborhood. They were flying insanely about and burning their wings, then dropping to unhappy, sizzling deaths in the hot grease.

Suddenly he became aware of a change. A wind was starting up again. Far off in the night, there rose a dull and rumbling sound, a strange roaring, almost like the boilers of a big steamboat at full speed ahead, but more so, and it seemed to be coming nearer, nearer.

Wind surged through the window and put out his candle. He got up and stepped outside, into a night suddenly wild with wind. A great tumult of steady roaring was passing nearby, but not touching New Salem itself, though the tremendous rush and suction accompanying the twister was wrenching off great oak limbs as if they were twigs. Chimneys flew, several window panes broke or were hurled inward by the vacuum. Abraham braced himself against the door frame.

Off in the distance, there had been thunder. Now, as the great wind passed, the storm gathered force and burst overhead. The lightning was blinding; the thunder racketed about as if it were going to rend heaven apart. Trees whipped madly in fresh gusts. Then the first great relieving drops of rain started down like shots, easing the tension. Abe ducked back into the store as hail came with the rain, until the roof seemed surely about to be beaten inward with the resounding bombardment, and he was almost deafened by the noise.

After that, it set in to pour. With some slackening, the rain let up about midnight, but it continued again, all the rest of the night. The air, fed by a wind out of the northwest, was blessedly cool and delicious to breathe and to live in.

In the morning, the flies, for the moment at least, seemed to have been drowned. The river had risen from the big run-off and, filled with sticks and leaves and drowned paroquets, as well as a couple of dead pigs and possums, was pouring with a pleasant rush over the dam again. Parched grass had already taken on a new look of life, and the village ducks and geese dabbled thankfully in puddles lying broadly across Main Street.

But the grasshopper-chewed corn in the fields was flattened where the big wind had passed—had raced so dangerously close to the cabins of New Salem. Much of that corn crop would be lost, good for nothing but fodder. Trees had been uprooted and flung headlong into the forest. New down-wood cluttered the foaming Sangamon.

When Matthew Marsh rode in to see how New Salem had fared, and to buy some coffee at Sam Hill's store, he said:

"I tell you, Lincoln, that there was the biggest wind I ever see! Ruined my cornfield, took down all my fencin', blew out all my windowlights, and killed two cows. And this mornin', when I was out to try and salvage my fence rails that had been tossed from here to Kingdom Come, what should I spy but two big wolves, monsters they looked to be, close as they was!"

"Wolves?" echoed Mrs. Onstot in frightened tones.

"Yes, wolves, ma'am," Marsh assured her. "I declare, they must have been no more than fifty yards from me, walkin' along as un-concerned-like, sort of dazed, as if they'd been blown from their den clean out into the middle of my cornfield and had to get home. I never seen nothin' to match it in all my days!"

"It was pretty bad right here, I'll admit," said Abraham, weighing out coffee beans into a bag. "Mr. Marsh, have you heard any-thing about the Rutledges? Ann's been sick and so is her daddy. Typhoid malaria, they call it."

"They're still pretty sick," put in Mrs. Onstot. "When I was out to pay a call day before yesterday, neither one knew me. Clean delirious."

"I'd better ride out and see," said Lincoln worriedly. "They're like my own family. Jimmy Short's been down sick, too. I ought to go see him, I guess."

"The road's pretty bad out that way," warned Marsh, picking up his bag of coffee. "The rain made it a swamp, and there's a lot of timber down, but a horse can make it, I reckon. Too bad about the Rutledges, ain't it, the trouble they've had lately."

Tall, thin, overworked Mrs. Rutledge said much the same thing to Abraham when he rode up that afternoon after the post office closed.

"It's been one calamity after another, Abe, ever since we lost the tavern," she said sadly. "The storm killed our best horse and twenty chickens, and I can't even find six of the young pigs, like as if they'd been blown clean away. Thank fortune, though, the cyclone didn't touch the house. Might have killed us all, and them in there so sick they couldn't have made it down to the storm cellar before the wind hit."

"How is Ann, Mrs. Rutledge? And Mr. Rutledge? I've been worried about them."

"Well, they're bad, Abe, very bad. I'm afraid to think what may happen. Doctor Allen comes out every day, but he can't seem to do much and, in the heat, they've felt worse and worse. It's hard to get cool water for them. This fresh air today—well, maybe it'll put new life into both of them. Go in, Abe, and say hello. But don't you stay too long. They get tired so easy."

Abraham was shocked at how thin and yellow James Rutledge looked, laid back on the rough, unbleached linen sheets of the big bed in the main room. His always prominent, strong jawbone and massive brow looked shorn of flesh, just bone under the yellowish skin.

"Howdy, Abe," he murmured, lifting one thin hand and letting it drop wearily. Abraham took it, feeling how dry and hot the skin was.

"It's good to see you, Mr. Rutledge," Abe began, not knowing what to talk about to this kindly, good man on whom the hand of death lay so plainly. "That was sure a storm last night, wasn't it?"

"I thought it was the Lord Himself calling me home, Abe," murmured James Rutledge, "though I reckon He wouldn't have had to make such a to-do to get me to come. I didn't know if He was sending me to the eternal fires or to the bliss of heaven, but I was so sick last night, I didn't care much which it was."

"Now, Mr. Rutledge, don't talk so!" Abraham was holding tightly to the thin, work-worn hand of the gray-haired man who lay so narrow and wasted under the coarse sheet. "You'll be with us a long time yet."

A small voice called weakly from the other room of the cabin. "Is that you, Abe? Come in here."

"Go and see my daughter, Abe. She's sicker than I am, son, and I'm fair worried about her."

Abraham, with a farewell clasp to the man's thin hand, got up and, in dread, walked to the door to see the red-haired girl lying small and pale on her bed. Her plaited hair looked rough and dull, without the light that used to sparkle from it, as it had sparkled from the girl herself.

His heart gave a sick flip-flop of fear at sight of that face. Not little Annie Rutledge! Older folk, maybe . . . but the young, the good, the dear . . . and there flashed again through his mind that never-buried memory of the time when his people and the neighbors were dying, the young and the old, the good and the bad, it didn't seem to matter. And that time when, for no apparent reason at all, his sister had died when her baby was born, and the baby with her.

He fought back the wave of fear, smiled at the girl on the bed. The hand under his strong fingers had nothing much to it but transparent skin and bones and blue veins showing through.

"Don't stay too long, Abe," said Mrs. Rutledge quietly from the doorway.

"Oh, Mama, let him stay, do," the girl cried petulantly, tears coming weakly to her eyes. "It's so lonesome here. . . ."

"They told me you were too sick to have visitors," began Lincoln, more at sea at knowing what to say to this poor child than to her father. "But if you feel like having me come, I'll be here every day, don't you fear."

"That would be nice, Abe," she murmured, her eyes closing and her breathing rasping suddenly. Her fingers moved aimlessly over the sheet, back and forth, as if hunting for something. Abraham, laying his hands on them to quiet their movement, felt the dry hotness in them.

"Abe," said Mrs. Rutledge despairingly from the doorway, "maybe you better go."

"Yes, ma'am," he said quietly. "I'll come back whenever you need me."

"There's naught you can do or the doctor either," she said, and her eyes held a look of tears not yet dried. "It's in the hands of the Lord. All we can do is pray."

Work went poorly after that. Abraham was too restless. Besides, he wasn't feeling very well himself. He was hot and feverish and had had several recurring spells of chills which boded no good, he knew. He'd had an attack of malaria when he boarded at the Camrons', several years ago, and had been nursed by all eleven of the Camron girls, which was a good deal of nursing for one young man. It didn't do him much good, though, when Doctor Allen gave them orders not to let their patient have too much water, and no amount of coaxing could make them break their word.

Abraham didn't relish the notion of another such bout coming on now, when he ought to be of some help to the Rutledges, if there was anything he ever could do. He'd been out twice, but both James Rutledge and his daughter were delirious and didn't know him. One of the married Rutledge daughters had come home to help her mother. Abe had brought some items of food from the store, but no one could appreciate them for a while, until the crisis was past.

He laid his head on the mail desk to ease the pain and tried to will health back into himself. He simply could not be sick, he couldn't, couldn't, couldn't . . . and he grew hotter and hotter with more than the summer's heat which had seeped back into the August countryside.

Jack Kelso found him there when he came running up on the store porch.

"Abe! Abe!" he cried, shaking the inert figure. Abraham, with a great effort, managed to lift his head. His eyes were dull with pain and fever. In his blurred vision, he seemed to see Jack as several great heads leaning over him.

"Hello, Jack," he muttered and tried to put his head down again.

"Listen! Abe, wake up! You *got* to listen!" cried Jack impatiently, shaking the bony shoulder again. "Little Annie Rutledge is dead. She went this morning and the news just came. Everyone in town's broken up about it. Sam Hill cried like a baby. I knew you'd want to know about it. You hear what I said, Abe? Ann— Ann's gone!"

Still Jack Kelso did not know whether his words penetrated or not.

"Thanks, Jack," was all Abraham said, forcing himself to his feet with a tremendous effort and standing upright. "Thanks for coming to tell me. Now go on, will you, and leave me alone?"

Rudeness like this was odd in Lincoln, but Kelso, feeling that the moment might be full of emotion to one as tenderhearted as Lincoln, and not realizing the state of the man's own illness, obeyed. Left alone, Abraham, in a half-conscious daze, started walking. From across the street, Mrs. Allen saw him go, but she thought nothing of it, except that he was walking oddly, like a sleep-walker. She saw him head blindly off into the timber back of the store and vanish in the big ravine where no one went in rattlesnake weather.

The silence of the trees was an echoing cavern, shadowy and green, with a purple gloom marked by late sunlight on the dark uprights of tree trunks. Cicadas burst into strident buzzing which rasped shrilly through Abraham's brain and he fought it, trying to escape the hot sound. But the ravine was a trap, with grapevines and wild yams catching him across the ankles . . . with a prickling of Spanish needles jabbing to the skin . . . they were pinpoints of pain, and then they dimmed to nothing in the rustle of leaves as he pushed through a tangle of hazel bushes.

He had been struggling forever with the jungle of whiplash hazel stems which struck his face and chest, caught his legs . . . a hundred determined demons holding him back . . . until, with a forward surge, like pushing through deep water in the Mississippi, he was out of the wilderness of hazels . . . and the plaintive, clear wailing of a wood pewee somewhere high in a honey locust cried over and over again, sadly, so that he could have wept . . . for what, he did not know, only that the bird's voice was full of the world's grief and his heart would sympathize with all grief . . . and he went on, and did not see the swift retreat of the bobwhite and her young, fleeing his uneven footsteps . . . and the bottom of the ravine was still muddy from the great storm . . . he stumbled over a fresh crayfish chimney, almost a foot high and very solid, and came down on his hands against the upward slope . . . he got up and went on, climbing, panting.

Pennyroyal was rank as he crushed it . . . stick-tights plastered his pants legs . . . a rattlesnake whirred its rattle and then, instead of striking, smoothly uncoiled and slid away with a dry rustle under the ferns . . . another rattlesnake lying supine on a log bent a cold and impersonal stare upon the figure fighting the vines, observed how he plunged headlong as his foot went into the entrance of a woodchuck's burrow, saw him lie there with his face against the cool moss . . . and the snake watched and made no move.

Somehow, it seemed to Lincoln as he lay there that he could never, never get to the top of the ravine, that he would continually slide back with every step . . . would always stay where he was, fighting vainly the wiry vines and the massive bushes, struggling against the Jo-Pye weeds whipping against his face . . . feeling blood trickling down his cheek where the catbrier slashed him . . .

The bird wailed and the snake watched as he lay on the slope. A tiger beetle scurried in a flash of iridescent blue over his hand and was gone. The cicadas stopped buzzing. The sun dropped behind the hill. The woods were growing still and cool; a blue dusk crept up from the hollows. The mosquitoes pricked him and still he did not move.

Night came into the ravine, night loud with whippoorwills. Up on the hill crest, a fox barked, lone and small in the summer dark. Far away, a dog yapped and the fox replied with small defiance. A baby cried up in the village; the children at Johnsons' cabin settled down with difficulty for sleep. Far off at Abells', a cow lowed long and mournfully for her calf.

A whippoorwill on quiet wings swerved through the darkness and paused on the hickory branch above his head. It was the bird's insistent hiccuping which wakened Abraham, though it was only a partial awakening. He was still burning with fever and the night, to his eyes, held a luminous glow which made the stars thrice their size and the fireflies uncertain blobs of golden light, coming and going.

He got to his feet and caught hold of vines and boughs and staggered to the top of the ravine . . . and went on . . . and on. . . .

Some time later, there was a feeble rap on the door of Judge Bowling Green's house. Judge Green, heaving his bulk out of his captain's chair, cautiously opened the door and held his candle high. No telling who or what at that time of night. . . .

Abraham Lincoln, leaning against the door jamb, slid in an inert mass to the floor.

"Mother!" Judge Green called to his wife, who, in her night gown and cap, hurried at the urgency of her husband's voice. "I don't know what ails him, but Abe's mighty sick and clean out of his head, seems like!"

It took some doing to get him off the floor and onto the bed, because, in spite of his illness, Abraham was as strong as ever and fought to keep the Greens from removing his muddy shoes and his torn shirt, to make him more comfortable. Finally, however, he grew quiet and slept, stretched across the bed at an angle so he would fit.

The Greens nursed Lincoln lovingly through a bad attack of malaria, trying to give him cool water on the days of his great fever, trying to keep him warm when the chills hit him and he shook so that his teeth rattled together, and he felt he would never be warm again.

And then, one morning, he was awake and rational, though weak as a young possum. His mind wasn't working very clearly, and he couldn't remember how he came there or why, nor what day it was, except that someone had come to say that Ann Rutledge had been taken by death. . . .

A little more than a week later, with his great reserve vitality, Lincoln was almost well again. He was thinner and quite yellow, but well, and back in the post office. He took on some surveying jobs. It was with relief that he learned that James Rutledge still lived. But somehow, Abraham felt, he would not be long in following his daughter. It was like losing part of himself to lose the Rutledges.

CHAPTER FIFTEEN

On a day in May, 1836, Harvey Ross brought a letter for Mrs. Bennett Abell, who was not at the post office to pick it up. In only a very few more days, the United States post office at New Salem, Illinois, would be closed, and Abraham Lincoln would be out of a job which had never really paid him very much. During his absences in Vandalia, Caleb Carman had substituted for him, but he had been glad to come back to his post.

New Salem was petering out, however. Each time he returned from Vandalia he could see it more plainly. Now not enough mail came to or went out of the village to make it worth-while for the mail carrier to take the trouble to climb the hill to deliver it or pick up outgoing mail.

Instead, people were moving to Petersburg, down in the bottoms, two miles north of New Salem. Family after family had gone.

And in May, word had come that the last mail delivery to New Salem would soon be made. Thereafter, the post office would be located at Petersburg.

The failure of the steamboat *Utility*, that same month, to ascend in the paddlewash of the ill-starred *Talisman* had sealed New Salem's fate, and the postmaster at Washington had pronounced its ultimate doom.

The *Utility* had foundered below New Salem, had stuck fast on a sandbar, where she was rapidly going to pieces. There was no hope of getting her off. Her engines, therefore, were removed and put to running the first steam mill at Petersburg. The *Utility* quietly and with finality fell apart as the river carried away her remains, and with them went the hope of a river future for towns along the cantankerous Sangamon. And there was no future at all for New Salem, perched too high above the river, too high above the main road, upon too narrow a peninsula of land.

"In a way, Lincoln," joked Jack Kelso when he heard the news, "I'd say it was all your fault, our losing the post office. If you hadn't surveyed Petersburg to make it a town, it wouldn't be the attraction it is. New Salem people might have stayed put and more would have come in, even without steamboats, especially if the roads were improved.

"But no, your chain and compass had to go gallivanting around down there to lay out a new town, and look how they take your post office away from New Salem and you! People are even moving their entire houses down there. I never saw the like!"

"Well, now, Jack, I wouldn't go so far as to blame Petersburg on me," protested Abraham, not certain whether or not Kelso were serious or joking. "After all, the town wasn't my idea. You recollect how Peter Lukins and George Warburton couldn't stand the gaff of the Temperance Society up here, or at least that's what folk say. Didn't enjoy being looked at and prayed over and lectured to and reformed when they'd no mind for such truck. You remember how, in some of their more lucid moments, they got mad and moved out and laid out a town of sorts for themselves down there. Named it Petersburg for Peter Lukins, though it could just as easily have been Georgetown, I reckon. Never did figure how they decided it. Didn't do that pair much good, though, I must admit, with George drowning himself in the Sangamon and Pete bursting a blood vessel."

"Yes, yes, I know all that. The fact remains, you made Petersburg properly into a town by platting and surveying it, and now look what happens. I hope you're satisfied! Anyway, New Salem is done for. No future up here, with no river business and the roads so bad, and the mill not having as much business, either, as it used to. Sam's carding machine still has business, but you could trust Sam Hill to make money during the plague. Where are you going when New Salem finally winks out, Lincoln?"

"Springfield, I suppose," Abraham answered with conviction. "You may not know it, but I've already bought a little piece of land in Springfield, with some extra cash I had. Imagine me! Bought it off Tom Edwards. Don't know what I'll do with it, but anyway, I've got a stake in Springfield now and probably will move there some day. Stuart wants me to come."

And so, just before the post office vanished, late in May, a letter came for Mrs. Bennett Abell. The handwriting on the cover looked suspiciously like that of Mary Owens of Kentucky. Thinking that surely Mrs. Abell would want to have her mail very, very quickly, Abraham shut up the post office and loped across the woods to the Abells' house.

"Why, thank you, Abraham," said Mrs. Abell cordially, taking the letter. "It was so kind of you to bring it all the way over here," she added, as she had done that other time, but now he knew there was no reason to peer back of her to discover a splendid vision behind her in the room. "It's from Mary, I see. She's been wanting me to visit her down in Kentucky and I think I shall do so this summer."

"That's nice," Abraham agreed. "And why don't you bring her back with you for a little visit here?"

Mrs. Abell laughed her pleasant, silvery laugh, which reminded Abraham so much of Mary's own mirth, but without the brittle edge.

"Now, that's an excellent idea, Mr. Lincoln, sir! Yes, I'll try to persuade my sister to come back with me, but on only one condition."

She paused, surveying him levelly, then said:

"Young man, if I bring Mary here, I want you to promise to marry her!"

Abraham's mind, like a skittish stallion, took a sudden leap of fright, as it always did when someone mentioned marriage to him. The very word somehow alarmed him with unknown tremors, though he could not have explained why. Then he righted himself so he could answer her joke with:

"Well, ma'am, you bring her back and I'll see to the marrying! That is, if she'll have me. I'd sure as fate want nothing more than to make her a good husband; but females are odd creatures sometimes, begging your pardon, Mrs. A. Might be she actually could turn me down!"

"Oh, no, I'm sure not!" Mrs. Abell assured him, delighted with her strategy.

At the ladies' sewing circle, the married women of New Salem had pondered just what sort of lure could make Abraham Lincoln ask a woman's hand in marriage, now that the Rutledge and Camron girls, as well as Parthena Nance, were all out of the way, and so few eligible young women remained. He was plenty old enough to have a wife, that was certain, and, as a legislator, he was a man of means and position. Mary Owens was suggested. They knew Abraham had sparked her in '33.

"Now don't you forget, Abraham Lincoln!" Elizabeth Abell reminded him. "You've promised. If I persuade Mary to return with me, it's up to you to do the rest!"

"Yes, ma'am, I sure will. I promise. And if I don't marry her, it'll not be my fault but hers for turning me down!"

The summer passed. The post office officially closed. There was a weedy, uncared-for look along New Salem's Main Street.

Lincoln announced himself as candidate for re-election to the State Legislature. His platform contained most of what it had held before, with a considerably startling addition. No one knew how on earth a man of Abraham Lincoln's sense and his wariness of women could have thought of it, much less included it in his political platform, but there it was:

I believe in all sharing the privileges of government who assist in bearing its burdens . . . admitting all whites to the rights of suffrage and by no means excluding females. . . .

"The idea, sayin' women should vote!" sputtered Henry Onstot to Joshua Miller, the blacksmith, and Martin Waddell, the hatter. "I never heard the like. Next thing you know, the females'll be runnin' for Congress and gettin' to be president of the *United*

States! I hope and trust I shall never live to see the day. Nor even the day my wife can make her mark on a ballot and decide who shall rule this land of ours! Women vote! It's an outrage!"

"Dangerous, too," put in short, heavy-set Miller, wiping his hands on his grimy blacksmith's apron. "You give a woman the reins and no tellin' where you'll end up."

"Oh, he won't get far with that part of his platform," assured Waddell. "Just sounds good, butterin' up to the ladies so they'll tell their husbands to vote for that charmin' Lincoln feller, because maybe some day he'll make a law that'll let 'em vote! Hah!"

On August 1, 1836, election day, while the votes were still coming in and the air was tense with the matter at hand, loungers on Sam Hill's store porch heard that long unheard sound, the swish of silk. Silken skirts rustled up the steps and through the doorway into the sudden darkness inside, where the polls were held.

"Why, how-do, ma'am!" exclaimed Sam Hill cordially, looking up boldly into her cool blue eyes below a smooth white brow and black curls, showing under a pale yellow leghorn bonnet. He noted that she had gained some weight and had lost a couple of teeth. "Welcome back. Did you come to cast your vote, too, ma'am?"

He laughed and the other men joined him, though not too uproariously because a lady was obviously present.

She was unruffled. "Well, Mr. Hill, perhaps you gentlemen won't let me vote this time, but mark my words, some day the time may come!"

The loungers frankly eyed her fine gown with the huge leg o' mutton sleeves and full skirt, her flowered bonnet, her neat kid slippers. Her voice made one man's heart turn quite over at sound of it.

"Miss Owens!" cried Abraham Lincoln, coming out of the back room. "I thought I was hearing things! It's you! You're a sight to make the angels shout! When did you get back?"

With a shock, he took in her additional size. In three years she had changed a good deal, though she still dressed so well and so neatly that her weight was not as unpleasant to view as it might have been.

"I came in yesterday on the stage from Springfield, sir," she said coolly, appraising him, too. He looked just a little better groomed, just a shade more mannerly and poised, though not a great deal. Maybe that was due to his experiences with other men in the Legislature.

"It's so good to be back. But I must not interfere with history. Will they re-elect you, Mr. Lincoln?" she asked tauntingly, daring him with her eyes to speak more intimately than he ever would with others present.

"Why, that's hard to tell, ma'am," he said serenely, standing his ground, his own level gray eyes daring her right back to say more. "When the polls close, I reckon we'll know the will of the people. Tonight, may I call on you, ma'am?"

"Yes, Mr. Lincoln," she answered demurely, a demon in her eyes. "You may."

For the next few weeks after he had won re-election, Abraham Lincoln and Mary Owens were seen everywhere together. The residents of New Salem, even in its more lively days, had never observed such an enthusiastic and concentrated courtship as they beheld in these two individuals, nor were they more puzzled as to the outcome.

"How could such a fine lady as her wed such a big, ungainly critter like that there Lincoln!" old Granny Spears exclaimed, bringing nose and chin together over her toothless gums to sip her cup of dittany tea.

"She ain't so much to look at herself, now. You note how fleshy she's got and losin' them two teeth has ruined her looks when she smiles," added Mrs. Johnson judiciously. Elmira Johnson had lost quite a lot of teeth herself, one for every child she had borne, and a few extra.

"Well, Lincoln's kind and good; he'd never knowingly hurt anyone, much less his wife. I vow, though, I'd wager she'll make him toe the line or know the reason why!" said Mrs. Kelso with a smile.

"*He'll* never ask her! He's a twitchy one with women, you take notice."

"He will if she eggs him on. You can see she's got her cap set for him. Her last chance to trap a man or she'll be an old maid the rest of her endurin' life, you can be sure of that. She ain't no spring chicken, you know!"

"With him in the Legislature and bound to be a lawyer in Springfield, Lincoln's headin' for a big future, no doubt, at least big enough to support a wife and young ones. More'n he'd ever be able to do here in New Salem, anyway."

"That's likely what she's got her eye on, I say."

"When you think he'll pop the question?"

No one could tell. Everyone watched. It was exciting to guess, but no one knew a thing. Nevertheless, Mary Owens and Abraham Lincoln were together every evening, either at the Abells' or over at the home of one of the cousins or connections where Mary might be visiting, or at Grahams'—and then he'd walk her home. Sometimes, however, she was very much irked by what he did or did not do. In walking through the woods, Abraham usually strode ahead in manly fashion, pioneer style, leaving her to pick her way as best she could over brush and logs. She said nothing, however, but burned in private over his uncouthness.

It was when the pair joined a group of other young people, all on horseback, riding to a barbecue out at Billy Greene's house, that matters came to a head. Girls and young men rode side by side, singing as they went, laughing, joking, holding hands across the space between the horses, occasionally riding closely enough to filch a kiss.

To cross the creek was a ticklish business, especially if a feminine rider were unsure of herself. The girls, experienced or not, shrieked at the way the horses splashed, so that their escorts came and guided the mounts to safety without slipping on the rocks of the ford.

All but Mr. Lincoln and Miss Owens. He rode his horse ahead, leaving Mary to cross the creek unattended. She was quite capable as a horsewoman—most Kentucky girls were—and handled her steed expertly. Nevertheless, she felt a rising anger burn within her. It was almost more than a woman could endure.

"Oh, there you are, Mary!" he called cheerfully as she rode up at last. "Thought you'd stayed behind and got lost!" he added, laughing.

"Little you would have cared if I had!" she snapped with unexpected venom. He had never heard such violence in her tones before.

"A gentleman would have helped his lady across! The others did. Only you—*you* had to ride ahead like a haughty Roman emperor, as if you hadn't seen me before in your life and cared less, while I splashed through as best I might. Look at my riding habit—muddy and a mess because of you, Abraham Lincoln!

"I could have broken my neck," she raged on, "and precious little it would have mattered to you! No, don't touch me!" she added as he came up contritely to take her hand. It fairly tingled to slap him hard.

"Oh, now, Mary, be reasonable," he pleaded. "You can ride. You're a better horsewoman than any girl in the crowd, and have more sense. I thought I was paying you a high compliment by letting you navigate the creek alone. I never thought—"

"No, you never thought!" she cried furiously, cheeks scarlet. "You never do! You seem to think I'm like those backwoods women you doubtless grew up with, self-sufficient as a man because they had to be and the men let them.

"I may be capable, but I like a little gentlemanly attention now and then! You would stop and tenderly help a hog out of a mudhole, or put young birds back in a nest, or defend the weak wherever you found them—you're considerate enough sometimes! —but there are times—oh, I boil to think of it! You remember when you and Mrs. Green and I were walking over to Greens' and Nancy was carrying her baby?"

"Well, yes, I recollect," said Lincoln, disturbed by her outpouring vehemence and not knowing in the slightest what to do about it. "I thought the baby cried an awful lot and was almighty loud."

"It was a warm day, and that hill was steep and brambly, and the mosquitoes like to ate us alive, but *you* marched on ahead, never minding us. The baby *was* fussy. I carried him for a bit, to ease her load, but you—you never once offered to be of help! You purely disgust me, Abraham Lincoln. Sometimes I think I never want to see you again!"

She urged her horse ahead to rejoin the crowd. As the party rode on, she fumed in silence. She refused to speak to Abraham. He meditated unhappily on what could set off some superior women in blazing tantrums like that and all over nothing. He honestly felt he was as much a gentleman as most fellows he knew. Maybe not as polished as John Stuart, but then, look at the differences in their upbringing and background. You'd expect Stuart to be a perfect gentleman and know how to act with ladies in any situation which presented itself, but would you figure rough old Abe Lincoln to have the same graces?

"No, by jing!" he exclaimed aloud, thumping the pommel of the saddle. His horse twitched its ears back at him and hastened its steps.

Casting an oblique glance at him after this brief outburst on his part, Mary maintained a heavy silence throughout the ride.

But at the party they unbent, and on the lovely moonlit ride home through the rustling autumn woods and the fragrant breezes of a prairie night, he made bold to reach across and take hold of her hand. She let him take it.

When at last he helped her down from her horse at Abells', he held her in his arms. She was a large armful, but he liked her like that.

"Mary, I know I'm a poor excuse for a man, but would you marry me anyway? It might be I'd improve if you took me in hand."

For a long moment she looked up at his earnest, thin face in the blazing light of a moon that was sailing middleways over a September sky flecked with racing white clouds. There was an excitement in the night, a restless urgency in clouds and wind.

"Give me a little time, Abraham," she said, a bit breathlessly.

"I'll have to think about it for a while."

With a quick pressure on his arms and a flashing smile, she went hurriedly into the house. Left standing outside, with his usual indecision, Lincoln could not figure out whether he was sorry or glad that she had not given him an answer. The weeks went by and still he did not receive word of any kind from her.

"She'll marry him, you mark my words," said Dulcena Good-pasture, placidly knitting.

"Ever since he passed that bar examination and has become a proper lawyer, she'd be a fool not to take him, rough as he is. You can overlook an awful lot in a man if he makes a good living."

"She's an old maid and likely not going to have too many more chances in this life to find her a man. She better take one whilst she can and don't let him get off the hook now."

"Oh, she will, she will. She's just playin' him, pretendin' to be hard to get. You take notice, though, she don't let her eyes off him when they're in a crowd and the other girls are about. That's why she come back, anyway, wasn't it?"

"Her sister, Lizzie Abell, says so. Said Mary was eager to wed that Lincoln and he, her. They don't seem in no hurry, though. At their age, they ain't got forever."

Certain of these conversations inevitably came to Lincoln's ears. Some confirmed his own opinions. He did feel that Mary was leading him on, yet holding back to be coy. She was keeping him dangling, but was eager to marry him, whether he was willing to or not. There were times when he felt he loved her terribly, and there were other times when he felt she was too old (she was a year older than he) and had gained far too much weight during her absence in Kentucky ever to be very attractive again. There were times when he wondered gloomily what on earth he had ever seen in her, and other times when they were together that he felt she was the fairest and dearest creature on earth, and all he could ever want in a wife. Meanwhile, he waited for her answer. And still the answer did not come.

CHAPTER SIXTEEN

MATTERS HAD GOTTEN exactly nowhere when Abraham Lincoln had to leave for Vandalia, in November, 1836. The 1834 suit of clothes still looked fairly impressive in New Salem but somewhat rusty and worn as compared with the nattier outfits of John Todd Stuart, Ninian Edwards, Orville Browning and others of his friends and constituents in Vandalia.

Although the State House had changed, it was not as improved as it might have been after all the trouble that had been taken to better its condition. Vandalia had heard the talk that it was time to move the capital to a more central spot. The people of the town, in order to keep the capital where it was and thus not drain away its annual source of prosperity, in desperation, tore down the old building and erected a new, two-story State House with a cupola. When the Legislature convened, however, these quarters were not yet completed. The unpleasant, dank atmosphere and smell of wet plaster permeated the place.

With John Stuart, who disconcertingly had been defeated for Congress in 1836 and now was the Internal Improvements Convention delegate, Abraham Lincoln inspected the new building. The two were somewhat gratified to find that it was still too small.

"The Vandalia people were smart enough to build a new capitol to keep us here," said Stuart, smiling. "But they should have been smart enough to build a State House that would have room for the ninety-one delegates of this session and allow for expansion with the years to come. If we are crowded in 1836, what will we be twenty years hence . . . fifty years! No, the capital city has got to be moved, and that will be our job in this session!"

"There's a great deal of talk about it already. Decatur wants it and so does Jacksonville," added Lincoln. "Stephen Douglas has been shouting about the location there. Alton wants it, wants to put the capital closer to St. Louis and have a Mississippi River port at the same time, and Springfield wants it badly, too. I reckon a whole lot of other towns would fancy the honor, if they'd thought of it in time. It looks like it will be quite a fight!"

Abraham Lincoln loved a fight. He had long since given up battling with his fists. Now he indulged in tighter, tougher mental combat. Political battles were something he could get his teeth into.

The nine representatives from Sangamon County were primed for any sort of fight. Not only were they the largest delegation from any county—some sparsely settled counties sharing a fourth or a third of a representative—but they were without much doubt the most united in their aims, as well as the tallest as a group of men. They became known as the Long Nine.

"If you'd lay us end to end, we'd stretch out all of fifty-four feet," Lincoln countered with a laugh when someone commented on the physical stature of the group.

Members of the Long Nine were agreed on fighting for a rail-road and on bringing to Springfield the state capital. With another election coming up in 1838, they could improve their outlook by pleasing people of their home county and home towns now while, at the same time, they maneuvered their political ends to bring about what they and the whole state must agree to.

But, in the session of 1836–37, the main topic of argument was not that of moving the capital, but the great Internal Improvements Bill. As a bill, it was not yet written; it was merely an expanding and explosive idea which grew bigger as men talked and argued and days passed. What went into it would depend upon the members at this session.

It would be a difficult bill to write, for Illinois, growing rapidly in population but far behind its census figures in its improvements, had a lot to demand of its legislators. Every county wanted some form of improved means of transportation—a canal, a navigable river, an improved road, a railroad—for without a better means of getting about, progress in the prairie state was doomed.

There was considerable opposition and argument among factions for and against the relative merits of railroads and canals, one pitted against the other. The trader, Gurdon Hubbard from near Chicago, who had made a fortune in furs among the Indians of that area, had come down to Vandalia to lobby for a railroad for Chicago, instead of the Illinois-Michigan Canal.

Hubbard was tall, handsome, magnetic and persuasive. He had lived with the Indians and had married one. He had brought along several striking Winnebago costumes. One day, to further his cause, he donned one of them and, beating a skin-covered drum, chanted a war song and danced a Winnebago war dance in the House chamber. Everyone, including Lincoln, thoroughly enjoyed this impromptu floor show and demanded encores. A good deal of hard pounding of the gavel on the Speaker's desk was required to get the men back to business.

In spite of such diversions, the Long Nine held to its carefully worked out plan. They were to vote for internal improvements— for an improved road here, for a bridge there, for a deepened river, for a canal or a railroad, whenever representatives from various counties should ask for them. In return for these votes, the Long Nine would ask for the support of these same representatives in bringing the capital to Springfield.

They would have to hurry. The Long Nine met until late hours, formulating their strategy. There was little time to lose because they must get their lobbying done before the Internal Improvements Bill was written. Here and there among the legislators—in the inn dining room, in a taproom, in the drafty corridors of the capitol building itself, wherever men were gathering after hours, Abraham Lincoln and eight other big men quietly but firmly circulated, promising to vote for a railroad line if its backer would vote for Springfield. . . .

"I should like to be the DeWitt Clinton of Illinois," Lincoln would say with his engaging, compelling humor, inserting himself into a group, "and give to this fair state the advantage of transportation which Clinton himself gave to New York State with the enviable Erie Canal. And it can be done, gentlemen, it *can* be done. With enough backing, your bill will go through. Now, Sangamon with its biggest delegation will gladly vote for your canal up near Chicago, for your railroad in Morgan, if you will favor us with a vote for Springfield as the next state capital. A centrally located, excellent town for the seat of government, you may be sure, gentlemen!"

"But Jacksonville—"

"Jacksonville needs a railroad, does it not?" Lincoln would say smoothly, almost sadly. "If you want a railroad, then why not concede the capital to Springfield and be certain that folk can get to and from your fine little town. . . ."

And so, after a good deal of high-pressure lobbying, talking, amending, rereading, more lobbying, promising, and finally voting, they passed the Internal Improvements Bill. Not every county got what it wanted. After all, funds were limited, and even these were largely on paper. Two long railroads bisecting the state were to be built, five rivers improved. The counties which benefited by neither were to have funds for roads. Almost everyone was happy.

On the night the bill went through, all Vandalia turned out into the January cold for a celebration. Great bonfires blazed to the snapping winter stars. Toasts were drunk in every tavern and taproom. Not everyone may have got what he wanted, but he had helped improve the sovereign state of Illinois, and that was something to shout over.

So far as the Long Nine were concerned, this piece of business was only the preliminary to the matter most deeply concerning the group from Sangamon. They could move around influencing men to vote for the various paper promises of the Internal Improvements Bill, but when the time came, the way might not prove so simple for the change of the capital.

First, a bill had to be written, presented and passed, legalizing the move from Vandalia elsewhere. This would be taken care of with a minimum of opposition and trouble because only the Vandalia people wanted to keep the capital where it was. But when the site of the new location must be decided, that was where the fight would come. During the passage of the first bill, Abraham Lincoln and certain other members of the Long Nine were absent from the floor, while they moved about among groups, working toward the Springfield vote.

After days of debate, in which Lincoln was foremost in thrusting the most telling arguments—days of disappointment and of tablings, of rereadings—the bill at last came to the Senate for a vote.

At first it seemed that nearly every man there was determined to make his home town the new state capital. No less than twenty towns were voted for, with Springfield ahead with thirty-five votes. Jacksonville had only fourteen, in spite of Stephen Douglas's hard work. Vandalia and Peoria tied with sixteen each. Alton had fifteen, Decatur only four, while the rest had three, two, or only one vote apiece. Railroad considerations—mere paper railroads as yet—influenced men from many counties to vote for Springfield. They felt that, out of loyalty to Lincoln and the Long Nine for helping them get their railroads, they should now assist in getting the capital moved to Springfield.

On the second ballot, Springfield's vote had risen to forty-four; on the third to fifty-three. By the fourth and last ballot, Springfield had won with a total of seventy-three votes. The Vandalia people were still stubbornly holding out for their home base, but they had never been considered as too serious an opposition. Vandalia as capital of Illinois was finished. The work of the Long Nine, exhausting and continuous and not always very aboveboard though it had been, had paid off at last!

There was a party that night at Ebenezer Capps's tavern, across the street from the doomed State House. The Long Nine, as hosts, invited all the members of the Legislature to attend. Lincoln, delighted at the prospect of a triumphal celebration, nevertheless felt a few qualms as to how he should pay for his share of the proceedings.

He watched the honorable legislators and their guests downing huge quantities of free oysters, a great luxury imported from Boston. He saw eighty-one bottles of expensive champagne emptied by

"MOTHER," JUDGE GREEN CALLED, "I DON'T KNOW WHAT AILS HIM, BUT ABE'S
MIGHTY SICK AND CLEAN OUT OF HIS HEAD, SEEMS LIKE!"

HE RODE HIS HORSE AHEAD, LEAVING MARY TO CROSS THE CREEK UNATTENDED. . . .
IT WAS ALMOST MORE THAN A WOMAN COULD ENDURE.

thirsty gentlemen whose voices had been raised in defense of Spring-field. There were free cigars of the best Havana tobacco for all, as well as quantities of nuts and raisins, salads, cakes and pies. There were no less than 110 members present, with a lot of hangers-on, townspeople, and strays who, scenting free food, came and ate their fill. Abraham was mentally trying to compute the astronomical figure of the bill, when the innkeeper presented it with a flourish to the Honorable Ninian W. Edwards.

It was, after all, Mr. Edward's party. The bill came to $223.50, almost as much as the Honorable Mr. Lincoln would make in his entire three months of service in the Legislature. But Mr. Edwards was a rich man and the sum was trifling to him. Mr. Edwards and his aristocratic ways—his nose lifted always as if in a slight sneer, his disgust with conditions in Vandalia and his casual mention of or flourishing of wealth and social position—always slightly irri-tated Lincoln. But the latter was wonderfully relieved and grateful that Mr. Edwards should pay for the triumphal celebration. There were, after all, some advantages to wealth and position!

Most of the important work of the session was over. A good many members went home, but Lincoln and the Long Nine stayed. There was a subject which had been worrying Lincoln for some time and he thought there might be an opportunity to present a bill now to do something about it.

Abraham Lincoln and Dan Stone, two of the Long Nine whose voices had been so powerful a few days before, entered their pro-test against slavery, on March 3, 1837.

"Slavery is founded both on injustice and bad policy," they declared. "It seems to me that abolition agitation tends to rather increase than abate its evils. Congress ought to have no power, however, to interfere with slavery in any of the states, but it does have the power to abolish slavery in the District of Columbia."

As if his voice had been uttered against the wind of a turbulent night, Abraham Lincoln's formal protest against the institution of slavery, which had vaguely disturbed him for a long time, went totally unnoticed.

No one was interested.

CHAPTER SEVENTEEN

WHEN THE Long Nine came in triumph to Springfield, there was a great bonfire near the town's whipping post in the public square. There were speeches and parades, drinks and banquets in honor of the men who had brought immortality to the mud-holes of Springfield.

When it was over, Lincoln knew that it was time to go out to New Salem and pick up his few belongings. There was nothing now to give him a living in the dying village, nothing to keep him there any longer . . . nothing but a certain young woman who was probably still visiting her sister north of New Salem.

She had never given him a final answer, neither yea nor nay, on the matter of matrimony. He had written to her many times from Vandalia and had received a few well written but not overly affectionate letters from her. They had bolstered him up immensely, however, especially on those days when he was feeling low in spirits.

He still could not figure out how he was going to improve a situation which he frequently wished himself well out of. He didn't want to hurt Mary Owens, for whom he had much affection, respect . . . and was it love . . . or what? He wished he knew.

There were times when he wondered desperately if he were really capable of loving any woman. Anyway, he heartily wished he had held his tongue on that lovely moonlit night and had never proposed, at least until he had had more time in which to think it over.

Living for months away from New Salem, in the whirl of Vandalia, with the glamour and charm of Orville Browning's new wife, as well as that of Elizabeth Todd Edwards and other ladies whose wit and beauty had added delight to the more prosaic atmosphere of the capital, had made New Salem and Mary Owens seem more dull and dowdy than ever.

Not that Mary was dowdy. She always looked well groomed, well turned out and dressed in the latest fashion. It seemed to him, however, when he paid a call on Mary, over at the Abells', on his return from the capital, that she seemed a trifle stouter than when he had seen her last. She looked so much older, too, but that may have been because he compared her with the very, very young Mrs. Browning.

Mary's eyes were just as blue, her black hair just as curling, her mind just as keen, her conversation just as rapier-sure as before, but he couldn't get over how she had changed. Or perhaps it was only he himself who had changed. He couldn't be sure. He only knew that he couldn't go on like this, not knowing what his future would be . . . if it would be with or without Mary Owens.

Abraham's horse, which had been stabled in Springfield during his absence in Vandalia, took him inexorably to New Salem and climbed the hill to the almost empty village, then continued on to the northwest, on the trail to the Abells' house. And she was there.

"Mary," he began desperately, taking her hand and leaping at once into the business on his mind. "Mary, I've just got to know. Will you marry me? What have you decided?"

Mary Owens smiled archly up at him and laid her other hand over his.

"You will have to give me just a little more time, Abraham," she said sweetly. "Just a little more time."

It was hopeless. She was determined to hold on to him just firmly enough so that he could not break away and be free, yet she would not commit herself. He felt trapped in quicksands, slogging desperately this way and that to escape, yet being sucked back again and again, grasping wildly at bushes, pulling himself out a little way, only to feel the entrapping sands still holding him.

In deep gloom he rode back to Springfield, to find a place in which to live.

This was not as simple a matter as he had hoped it would be. At New Salem, although Lincoln had never lived in any place he could call his own, he felt that he had many homes, as many as there were cabins in the village and out beyond. Everyone was his friend. Everyone invited him to eat and sleep whenever he needed it. At times he had boarded at the tavern or at the Camrons' but it had never strained his pocketbook.

But in Springfield it was different. For one thing, the town was so much bigger. He knew a few people, but not many. It was lonesome to walk along a street and not recognize a soul, nor have anyone hail him and stop to talk. Besides, finding a place to stay meant forking over his hard-earned pay regularly, and after a few inquiries at boardinghouses and at the Globe Tavern, he was afraid he would have to camp out in the woods if he wanted a place to sleep.

Thinking that, if he had his own furniture, he could rent an empty room for less, he went to young Joshua Speed's store, to ask the price of bedclothes and a bedstead of the plainest sort, but the sum Speed asked discouraged him.

"It's too dear, Speed, I'm sorry," Lincoln said in a state of gloom. "I reckon I'll have to think of something else."

"What's the matter, Lincoln?" asked Speed, who was handsome and well educated. His store was a gathering place for other young men of the town; his rooms upstairs were an evening meeting spot for fellowship and conversation. "Can I help you out?"

"Well, Speed, it's just this. I've got to have a place to live if I'm to work in Springfield, but until I can make regular wages on some law cases, I'm too poor to pay the prices landlords are asking, and I can't even buy the fittings to sleep on. I reckon I'll have to try somewhere else, thank you kindly, Speed."

The friendly young merchant smiled. He put out a detaining hand.

"Look here, Lincoln. No need to hunt farther. I've got a big room upstairs. Some of my clerks sleep there. If you think you could put up with me and my ways, you're welcome to camp there for as long as you want. What do you say?"

A lovely light shone over Abraham's lean face and his hand shot out to grasp that of Josh Speed. Springfield, after all, was very much like New Salem.

"I say that's just bully!" cried Lincoln. "You've got a roomer, Speed. Wait till I get my saddlebags, and I'll be moved!"

Abraham Lincoln settled down in Springfield. He took a few minor cases which came to John Stuart's firm, and with each one, he felt a greater sense of power and confidence. Still and always, however, plaguing him night and day when nothing else could contrive to crowd the thought out of his mind, was Mary Owens and the answer which she never gave.

Not until the following autumn, 1837, would she finally reply. "Have you decided, Mary?"

"Yes, Abraham," she began, and his heart set up a faster pounding. Here it was at last! "I have decided." There was a long pause in which he was sure she could hear his heart hammering.

"I'm sorry, but I really do not wish to marry you. It was hard to make up my mind because I am really very fond of you. But I know this will be better for both of us. We could never be happy together. Good-bye, and God bless you."

The blow was between the eyes and Abraham blinked, looking down at her, not quite comprehending the full import of what she had said. He had felt so sure that he knew what it was going to be.

"You won't—?"

He realized he hadn't known until this moment that he loved her so much. In the searing impact of losing her, he began to understand that he had been in love all this time, in his own clumsy way, and on being given the freedom which for so long he had felt was his sole wish in life, he wanted only to be enthralled forever.

He let his horse find the way back to Springfield, as he unhappily tried to figure out why and where he had failed.

CHAPTER EIGHTEEN

A MONTH LATER, in November, when Abraham Lincoln was certain that Mary Owens had gone back to Kentucky, he ventured to ride over to pay a visit to the Greens, who still lived outside the defunct village.

It was painful to move along the haunted, grass-grown street which once had known so much activity. Only a handful of people still remained, and they would leave soon. It seemed that half his life lay buried in the gaping cellar-holes where cabins had been taken away, to be rebuilt down in Petersburg. There were memories, too, in the run-down tavern and other familiar spots which still stood. He knew he should not have come—it made him too sad—but he was lonely for a talk with Judge Green and some of the others with whom he had once had so many rousing good evenings of argument and conversation.

But the conversation that night was not pleasant nor happy.

"What is going to happen to the nation anyway?" Mentor Graham exclaimed bitterly, scowling under his sandy-red eyebrows. "It's getting worse instead of better and how it will end scares me to think of it!"

"Slavery is a sin against God and man," pointed out Doctor Allen, who, as a New Englander, was violently opposed to slavery.

The Reverend Berry nodded vigorous agreement.

"It's against the Constitution of the United States, against democracy, against all the principles laid down by the founding fathers!" the doctor went on soberly. "How can we make bold to call ourselves good Americans when we permit slavery in our land?"

The others nodded, their faces serious and worried.

"We read, 'All men are created equal . . . the right to life, liberty and the pursuit of happiness,' Doctor Allen went on. "But I figure that these are only hollow sentiments when we do not keep them, or when we limit them only to certain members of the human race. It is a disgrace in the face of the world that we hold human beings in bondage in a land settled for and by free men!"

"Well, but how can you stop slavery now?" asked Lincoln, flinging out both big hands in an anguished sort of gesture. "How can you stop a tidal wave, destroy a mountain, dry up a sea?"

"Slavery is man-made," pointed out Doctor Abell quietly. "And what man has created, man can destroy."

"Perhaps," assented Lincoln, looking at the floor. "I know that America can't keep on being half slave and half free without destroying one part or the other of itself! We've *got* slavery; man-made or not, it's here. It's like a disease, a horrible, disfiguring mutilation, but we've got it and I believe it would rend the nation apart to attempt to abolish it now!"

"We chased out the British when they had our country," Judge Bowling Green defended his cause, puffing on his pipe. "It was a bad fight and a long one. It killed a lot of our people and theirs, and almost ruined the economy of a new nation. It had every reason in the world to be a losing battle—we puny ones against the whole British Empire and the Hessian mercenaries thrown in! We likely might have failed, but we went in and cleaned them out and made us a United States."

"This is hardly the same," commented Mentor Graham drily.

"Well, anyway," went on Green, standing up for his point. "It was the British who brought the slaves here in the beginning, and they ought to have been sent back at that time. That's what we need to do about slavery—wipe it out, make it illegal, destroy it, once and for all, be a clean, pure nation . . . if we were men and didn't take the South's dictates as law."

"How are you going to go about ending slavery, Judge?" Abraham broke in petulantly, almost angry. "It isn't like chasing out the British, as Graham mentioned. They were white men, free men, with homes over the seas. They were mighty glad to give up and go home, I reckon.

"It isn't that easy with the Negroes. We brought them here— we or the British, it doesn't really matter now. They didn't come because they wanted to or because they wanted to conquer and rule our land. We captured them as if they were wild animals and sold them like animals, as if they had no human feelings or sensibilities. We've kept most of them from getting an education and living like upright human beings. I saw some of it in the South and it sickened me!"

Lincoln paused, remembering the slave market in New Orleans; the runaway slave, Caleb, who had ridden on the flatboat with him and his companions a little way, to escape dogs and men who were on his trail; remembered dimly, as if in an endless passageway into the past, how his mother used to talk against slavery.

"America has a responsibility to these poor people," he went on, thinking as he went. "If we should end slavery, what would happen? They would be free, and what is freedom to a former slave? Would he know how to work for himself, make a living, he who has been thought for and taken care of by his master all his life? Gentlemen, it's a mighty touchy subject. An awful lot of men are getting involved in it, and I reckon there'll be a whole lot of trouble before they're through, if they ever are."

Abraham put his head in his hands and rubbed his skull, as if to massage ideas into it, until all his coarse black hair stood up as though a wind had whipped through it.

"Well, it's not your problem, nor ours, either, I guess," soothed Doctor Abell. "The nation has handled slavery longer than we have lived, and I suppose it will continue to do so long after we are all forgotten."

"Yes, but it *is* our problem," contradicted Lincoln. "Look, there are all those things that are happening now that didn't happen before. Abolition isn't the solution, but men like Garrison are sure trying hard and getting hurt for their pains."

"Yes, I recall that incident about a man down in Petersburg, Virginia, who was whipped and driven out of town a few years ago," put in Judge Green, "all because he said that the blacks, as men, were entitled to their freedom and ought to be emancipated."

"They've been tarring and feathering men for subscribing to abolition papers," went on Lincoln. "They're trying to forbid abolitionist meetings. It all adds up to awful trouble. I read, too, that editor Lovejoy has finally had to move his press out of St. Louis to Alton, because he printed abolitionist propaganda, and now they've already torn up and thrown his press into the river! And this in Illinois, mind you!"

"Elijah Lovejoy acted like a fool," declared the Reverend Berry warmly. "He baits his enemies with high-flown oratory in his newspaper and throws abolitionist nonsense into their teeth, then howls when they set upon him to retaliate!"

"If abolition isn't the solution to the problem, then what is?" inquired Doctor Allen mildly as Mrs. Green quietly passed cups of fresh, hot coffee to the guests.

Lincoln helped himself to a crisp Baldwin apple from the bowl on the table.

"Well, it seems that if better minds than ours haven't found the solution, it's hardly up to us," put in Abraham, munching loudly on the apple. "But it does seem to me that at least slavery could be kept out of the new territories. It should be kept in the South where it's always been, and prevented from spreading as the nation grows. Before long, the whole of America all the way to the Pacific will become part of the United States. If slavery goes into all that tremendous area, the North and its principles will be overridden and we'll become a slave-owning nation!"

"You paint a horrid picture, Lincoln," put in Graham sarcastically. "What do you suggest to prevent it?"

"I have no suggestion," went on Lincoln. "It's the South's problem. We would have their everlasting hatred if we should abolish slavery and destroy their economy. I doubt if the South could exist without slaves. I just don't think it ought to be allowed to spread, though . . ."

There came a sudden knocking at the door. Breathless, Jack Kelso burst in.

"I just heard! They've killed Lovejoy down at Alton!" he cried, sinking into a chair, out of breath from his run across the woods, up and down a hill and a ravine. "Harvey Ross brought the news from Springfield. Three days ago—they threw Lovejoy's fourth printing press into the Mississippi River. They'd broken up and destroyed his three other ones, as fast as he got them. This one was stored in a warehouse down near the river. They broke in, tore it apart, threw the whole thing into the water, and then the mob besieged Mr. Lovejoy and his friends. They were held at bay like animals in that warehouse!"

Abraham, who always came to a slow boil inside when he heard of the persecution of men or animals, sat forward in his chair, hands gripped between his knees, his lips tight.

"Go on," he said.

"Well," continued Kelso, "there were shots, and several men were killed. They shot Lovejoy, carefully and on purpose. Killed him like a dog. And next day they had a trial—a trial, they call it! A farce! The men who did all the damage and murdered a fine man were all acquitted. And they call it justice!"

The men sat silently after their first exclamations. There was so little anybody could say. None of them were personally acquainted with Elijah P. Lovejoy, newspaper editor of St. Louis, but they felt personally stunned by the tragedy. It was not the death of one man, it was an attack on human liberty, on the right of free speech, on the freedom of the press.

"Freedom of the press," said Abraham Lincoln, to no one in particular. "Freedom! Good night, all." And he got up, put on his coat and wrapped a length of comforter around his neck, put on his tall hat, shook hands all around, nodded to Mrs. Green, who watched him anxiously, and went out into the dark November night. Pondering, deep in thought under the silent winter stars and the chill light of a half moon frosting the prairie, Abraham Lincoln headed toward Springfield. A hunting fox loped across the road in front of his horse, which shied slightly but resumed its steady gait. Frontier horses were accustomed to small surprises like foxes and prairie wolves, or the sudden roar of prairie chickens starting up. The November night was glistening with heavy white frost under the setting moon before he rode into Springfield and came to Speed's lodging place.

Several months later, on a crisp January night in 1838, Abraham Lincoln, as guest speaker, got up to address the Young Men's Lyceum in Springfield. His suit was well brushed and his shoes were blacked and polished. He had planned and written out and memorized what he was going to say. He would pound home some of the facts of this bitter period in which some men were growing fearful of expressing their views.

"In the great journal of things happening under the sun," he began, looking down at the interested young masculine faces before him in the drafty hall, "we, the American People, find our account running, under the date of the nineteenth century of the Christian Era. We find ourselves in the peaceful possession of the fairest portion of the earth, as regards extent of territory, fertility of soil, and salubrity of climate. . . . We, when mounting the stage of existence, found ourselves the legal inheritors of these fundamental blessings. We toiled not in the acquirement or establishment of them—they are a legacy bequeathed us by a *once* hardy, brave and patriotic, but *now* lamented and departed race of ancestors. Theirs was a task (and nobly they performed it) to possess themselves and through themselves, us, of this goodly land; and to uprear upon its hills and its valleys, a political edifice of liberty and equal rights; . . . this task of gratitude to our fathers, justice to ourselves, duty to posterity, and love for our species in general, all imperatively require us faithfully to perform.

"How, then, shall we perform it? At what point shall we expect the approach of danger? By what means shall we fortify against it? Shall we expect some transatlantic military giant, to step the Ocean, and crush us at a blow? Never! All the armies of Europe, Asia and Africa combined, with all the treasure of the earth (our own excepted) in their military chest; with a Bonaparte for a commander, could not by force, take a drink from the Ohio, or make a track on the Blue Ridge, in a trial of a thousand years."

He paused, and the young men clapped heartily.

"At what point then is the approach of danger to be expected?

I answer, if it ever reach us, it must spring up amongst us. It cannot come from abroad. If destruction be our lot, we must ourselves be its author and finisher. As a nation of freemen, we must live through all time, or die by suicide."

Again the audience burst into applause, this time hardly before he had put his period. He bowed, acknowledged their approval.

"I hope I am over wary;" he continued, "but if I am not, there is, even now, something of ill-omen amongst us. I mean the increasing disregard for law which pervades the country; the growing disposition to substitute the wild and furious passions, in lieu of the sober judgment of Courts, and the worse than savage mobs, for the executive ministers of justice. . . . Accounts of outrages committed by mobs, form the everyday news of the times. They have pervaded the country, from New England to Louisiana. . . .

"It would be tedious as well as useless to recount the horrors of all of them. Those happening in the State of Mississippi, and at St. Louis, are, perhaps, the most dangerous in example, and revolting to humanity. . . . In the Mississippi case, they first commenced hanging gamblers . . . next, Negroes . . . then white men supposed to be in league with Negroes, and finally strangers . . . till dead men were seen literally dangling from the boughs of the trees . . . in numbers almost sufficient to rival the native Spanish moss of the country, as a drapery of the forest.

"Turn, then, to that horror-striking scene at St. Louis. A single victim was only sacrificed there. His story is very short; and is, perhaps the most highly tragic. . . . A mulatto man . . . was seized in the street, dragged to the suburbs of the city, chained to a tree, and actually burned to death; and all within a single hour from the time he had been a freeman, attending to his own business, and at peace with the world."

As he developed his speech and watched the mobile young faces below him swayed with the tragedy he told, Abraham Lincoln could feel once again a rising tide of anger, grief and desperation working within himself. He was only a young and not too prosperous lawyer, but he felt almost as if the terrible plight of the whole nation were saddled upon his shoulders.

The ghost of Elijah P. Lovejoy was present and ever with him, resting upon his soul and upon his conscience as he felt it must rest upon everyone in that hall, a public conscience gibbering from every man's bed post until the wrong was made right.

"By the operation of this mobocratic spirit, which all must admit, is now abroad in the land," he went on, "the strongest bulwark . . . of any Government . . . may effectually be broken down and destroyed. . . . Whenever the vicious portion of population shall be permitted to gather in bands of hundreds and thousands, and burn churches, ravage and rob provision stores, throw printing presses into rivers, shoot editors, and hang and burn obnoxious persons at pleasure, and with impunity; depend upon it, this Government cannot last! . . .

"The question recurs, 'how shall we fortify against it?' The answer is simple. Let every American, every lover of liberty, every well wisher to his posterity, swear by the blood of the Revolution, never to violate in the least particular, the laws of the country; and never to tolerate their violation by others. As the patriots of seventy-six did to the support of the Declaration of Independence, so to the support of the Constitution and Laws, let every American pledge his life, his property, and his sacred honor. . . . Let reverence for the laws be breathed by every American mother, to the lisping babe that prattles in her lap—let it be taught in schools, in seminaries, and in colleges;—let it be written in Primers, spelling books, and in Almanacs;—let it be preached from the pulpit, proclaimed in legislative halls, and enforced in courts of justice. And, in short, let it become the *political religion* of the nation. . . ."

It was over and the young men were crowding around to shake his hand and thank him for his stirring and inspiring address.

Next day, he received a letter of thanks from the president of the Lyceum, with a request for a copy of his address to print in the newspaper.

He had composed it sketchily in the beginning, on scraps of paper, until he had it in his mind, but he thought he could write it out about as he had said it, perhaps polishing it up here and there, which was easier to do on paper than when he was speaking. It was printed in the *Sangamo Journal*, on February 3, 1838. He rather liked the appearance of it, but felt he might have done better here and there.

CHAPTER NINETEEN

ABRAHAM LINCOLN felt he had never been more lonely in all his life. It was a very different quality of loneliness than he had known when he was on the river or by himself in the woods. He had enjoyed that, had talked aloud to himself and to the wild things, had done a lot of thinking. But loneliness in a city, he found, was different. Coupled with it was his feeling of inferiority and his ignorance of social behavior, something the woods had never taught him.

Aside from providing a means of making a living, life in the new capital was not as entertaining nor as fascinating as Abraham had figured. It seemed to him, sometimes, that he had enjoyed himself far more in New Salem. At least everyone knew him there, and he them. There was life in New Salem and he was part of it. In Springfield—well, he guessed the life was there, but he seemed to be more on the outside, looking in.

He was acquainted with politicians and lawmakers at the slowly rising, new stone State House, but hardly any of them ever invited him to come home to supper and spend the night—not they! He had met no ladies. Only one, he moped, had spoken to him since his arrival, and she had only opened her mouth because she had to, since he was clumsily standing on the hem of her gown and she could not move away from his neighborhood until he stepped off.

Sometimes he wished he had had the sense to make Mary Owens his wife, so he could have her here with him. Yet she, who loved fine things, would have had to sit by and watch other ladies, noses in air, flourishing about in carriages without being able to join them as an equal. He felt she would have had a hard time bearing his poverty with grace and patience, and he knew also that she had been wise in refusing him. For that matter, the kind of woman he wanted for a wife *would* feel that way. And his thoughts churned unhappily and got him nowhere.

Loneliness, therefore, besieged Abraham night and day. Living with Joshua Speed helped matters very little. Speed was the melancholy, introspective sort himself. Still, he was young, slim, wonderfully handsome, striking, with his black eyebrows and expressive mouth, and he had money. Most of the girls sighed over him, wrote rhapsodic pages about him in their secret diaries, were thrilled when he singled out one of them to escort to parties or plays. Joshua Speed was always getting involved in fleeting love affairs which he somehow got out of with brisk dispatch when he discovered how seriously they were trending. He seemed just as unsure of himself as Abraham, however, just as much afraid of getting involved in marriage, yet often he was just as eager for it.

"If I could be assured that I would be a proper husband, if I felt I knew how to act with a woman," Speed might exclaim to his sympathetic friend, "could support her in comfort, nurse her in sickness, and still retain my individuality, my own life, I might consider it, but it just seems too much for a man to take on, blindly like that. How can a bachelor know how to be a husband?"

And Speed would pace, and Lincoln would try to convince him that he really was a fine, conscientious fellow and any girl should be proud to marry him. Lincoln had observed, besides, that any number of them would gladly take on that charming prospect any time the skittish Speed popped the question.

And so young Speed would be cheered up. Then perhaps the very next day he would have the task of trying to brighten Lincoln's melancholy heart and long countenance. Oftener, though, Abraham went out alone, night after night, just walking. While the dogs of Springfield were barking to a sailing moon, and an urgent wind blew mysterious messages past the trees and gardens, he walked the slippery plank sidewalks until they ended. He kept on walking over the new spring grass, trampling down the closed-up spring beauties where woods had been but lately shorn, cracking off mayapple umbrellas, hearing the frogs chorusing and jingling in the ditches and trying to ponder the mysteries of life, love and man on earth. He never resolved very much but came home late, shoes muddy, hair on end, to crawl in beside Josh Speed, who was already long asleep. Sometimes Abraham lay awake, still thinking, until morning.

He was, however, making enough to live on. He was earning more than he ever had in his life. His debts were paid. The "National Debt" was finally all cleared away to the last penny. Law cases, not all of which he won, and not all of which were paid for, were coming along. He was appointed to the Circuit Court, which meant going to one town and then another during the period of the judicial circuit and holding forth as a lawyer. His equipment, legal papers and files were contained in his worn saddlebags and in his tall hat.

Riding the circuit was interesting and a change. Abraham liked it. He became acquainted with more towns in Illinois than he had visited before, met more people, made more friends, ran into more different kinds of human troubles that had to be ironed out with wit, wisdom and judicial pondering, than ever before. Work took his mind off his inner unrest, loneliness and feeling of inferiority, and he was thankful for that.

Work and brooding, however, did little to help Abraham's low moods. He needed to be with people. He and some of the other young men of Springfield felt they might enliven the dull course of events if enough young ladies should be persuaded to attend the initial session of the Legislature, when it opened for the first time in Springfield. That town's society had a solid core of respectability and elegance, including some very personable young ladies, but there were hardly enough of them. Besides, there were certain charming girls who were very much missed by the legislative gentlemen, who remembered the gay times in Vandalia.

If the very young Mrs. Browning could be cajoled into coming from Quincy with her husband and bringing along her charming sisters and any other eligible young ladies who might find Springfield's social season enjoyable . . .

"It's the best way I can think of to get a little life into this place," concluded Lincoln, spokesman for the group of young men who usually gathered nightly in Speed's rooms to talk. Abraham took up a pen and started to write—most matters, he felt, could be solved by writing. He liked to pen anonymous letters to the newspapers, in defense of some special subject or to right a wrong, and he often indulged in poetry of some length. Now he would turn his talents to composing a letter which might bring the ladies to Springfield.

He addressed it politely, yet a trifle humorously, to the Honorable Mrs. Browning, and when completed, it was enthusiastically approved and signed by half a dozen eager and eligible young gentlemen. It was sent off on the next mail stage to Quincy.

If there was anything which the charming Mrs. Browning loved it was attention from plenty of pleasant and adoring gentlemen. Before long, therefore, Springfield received word that she and her entourage were indeed on their way.

In a delighted flurry, Lincoln and his friends planned a splendid party, a cotillion, for which special printed invitations were issued. It would be held at the American House on the night of December 16, 1839, and the invitations were signed by sixteen gentlemen, including Joshua Speed, Stephen Douglas, James Shields and Abraham Lincoln.

The cotillion was a tremendous success. The food was delicious, the music the best that was to be had in Springfield. The social set of the town and its influx of new people, the wives and cousins and sisters of the lawmakers, including Mrs. Browning and her sisters, were all there.

The ladies were in their finest gowns obtainable outside New York and New Orleans. The men were sleek in broadcloth and high stocks and varnished boots. Lincoln had a new suit, his first after that splendid affair in which he had made his debut in politics. His shoes were as glossy and as tight and as uncomfortable as anyone could wish; they pained him considerably all evening.

The dancing was already underway when Ninian Edwards was announced. The Honorable Mr. Edwards, son of the first and only territorial governor of Illinois, his head held at an aristocratic angle, his clothes impeccable, made a most impressive entrance. His handsome and imperious wife, Elizabeth Todd Edwards, cousin of John Todd Stuart, was on his arm. The Edwardses arrived later than most of the other guests. Elizabeth felt that this was fashionable and in excellent taste. Besides, one made a far better entrance that way. As social arbiter of Springfield, Elizabeth Edwards set fashions; she did not follow them.

Beside her walked a small, beautifully dressed girl with coppery-brown hair ornamented with flowers and pearls. Her wide-skirted gown was of the most stylish mode, leaving the shoulders bare. The high color of excitement pinked the stranger's lovely complexion with an extremely becoming flush.

Mary Todd had come up from Kentucky, as her sisters had done before her, to find a husband. Elizabeth, the eldest, had done extremely well; so had Frances, the next in line. Mary, the most self-willed and determined, had only recently come to Springfield on an extended visit which had but a single aim—though one did not say so baldly, of course.

Mary had already met a number of pleasant and eligible gentlemen. One was little Stephen A. Douglas, who, discovering the late arrivals, paused for a certain effect in the doorway, hurried up to greet them.

"My dear Miss Todd!" he exclaimed rapturously, taking her plump, gloved hand in his and bending low over it, all the while keeping his eyes on her face. This was not difficult, since both Miss Todd and Mr. Douglas were about the same height.

"May I have the honor of this dance, dear Miss Todd?" he begged, as the orchestra again struck up the music. The maid had scarcely taken her cloak, when he swept her off. Stephen Douglas was an expert dancer and so was Mary Todd.

He and the other young men kept Mary busy all evening. The dances were all very familiar to her, for she had graduated from Madame Mentelle's finishing school, in Lexington, and could not be ill at ease in any event which the Sangamon country could produce.

She was witty, she was charming, she glowed, she sparkled, her feet wore wings, she laughed—wit with an edge to it, charm with calculation, a glow with conscious knowledge of beauty behind it, agility with an awareness of superiority, laughter quite often at someone else's expense. It was all so neatly done that one could not quite pin the stigma of unkindness upon her, yet often felt its hidden barbs. Mary, however, loved a party. She had a delightful evening.

Miss Todd had not met Mr. Lincoln. Coming in so late, there had not been an opportunity for all the hosts to be presented. Besides, Mr. Lincoln was not one whom Ninian Edwards had invited to his home to meet his womenfolk.

Abraham, meanwhile, had spent the evening happily circulating among the guests. He had devoted some time to dancing very poorly with the charming sisters of the fascinating Mrs. Browning, as well as with that kindly lady herself. She was by far the most talented woman in the charm department that Lincoln or any of the others had ever known.

The women liked her, too, and the men certainly made fools of themselves over her, some of the stout old ladies whispered behind their fans. Her adoring husband, Orville Browning, smiling at everybody, considered himself the luckiest man in Illinois, if not the nation.

Mary Todd became aware of Mr. Lincoln when a giant bean-pole figure, in a new suit which somehow didn't fit properly in the right places, struggled past with a tolerant partner in his arms. The partner usually was laughing at something he had said and was trying at the same time to avoid being trampled by his unskilled feet.

Abraham was mentally berating himself for having neglected learning how to dance properly. He could walk all the way from Springfield to New Salem and not get winded, but trying to navigate a ballroom with a feminine partner in billowing skirts wore

173

him out, confused him dreadfully, made him lightheaded and left him breathless. Besides, his shoes pinched terribly and grew worse as the evening grew warmer, the activity more stirring.

Mary Todd, casting her eyes around the room, was satisfied that she had made an impression upon just about every gentleman present, and had made every lady there, with the possible exception of Mrs. Browning, look at her with a degree of envy and irritation. At last, she focused on the tall beanpole with the awkward feet.

"Who is that man?" she asked Ninian Edwards, who had just brought her an ice.

"Where? Oh—why, that's Lincoln. Abraham Lincoln. I thought you knew him. You've surely heard of the fellow. I've sung his praises for years. In the Legislature four terms, an able lawyer. Not much money and certainly no family background worth mentioning—backwoods farmers, from what I hear—but he's got an excellent brain, good reasoning power. Stuart thinks the world of him. Got sense, my dear. Charm, too, though you'd never think it to look at him."

"Pray introduce him to me, sir! You have been remiss in keeping me away from this man with no background and much charm!" Laughing, she waited in her chair as Ninian Edwards, indulging his imperious sister-in-law, went up to the knot of men surrounding a figure who sat, long legs crossed, resting his feet, regaling his friends with a story.

With compelling dignity, Ninian Edwards firmly detached Lincoln from the appreciative group and returned to Mary with him in tow.

"Miss Todd, may I present Mr. Lincoln? Mr. Lincoln, my sister-in-law, Miss Mary Todd of Lexington. Two such fine intellects should have the pleasure of each other's company!"

With this thrust, and ignoring his wife's glare, Ninian Edwards turned and strode off. The music started up again, and Abraham decided there was no help for it—in some embarrassment, he asked Mary to dance.

It was not a highly successful performance. She was too short for so tall a partner, and he didn't know how to hold her properly.

They endured the entire figure, struggling uncomfortably around the floor, then thankfully retired to a couch and talked.

"You can see I'm a poor one at this sort of thing," apologized Lincoln, mopping his perspiring forehead. "I hope I didn't hurt you that time when I stepped on your foot."

"Not at all, sir," said Mary agreeably, though her foot pained her unpleasantly. "I can see I shall have to teach you the art of the dance!"

"I doubt if it would do much good, ma'am," he said hopelessly. "I'm too old to make these long pins of mine behave in any way but what they've been doing all these years. But I thank you kindly."

He sensed someone staring at him, and turned around quickly enough to catch the eyes of Elizabeth Todd Edwards, across the room, frowning at him in a most disconcertingly severe manner.

"I reckon Mrs. Edwards thinks I've kept you away too long, ma'am. I'm sorry," he apologized again. "Let me take you over to her."

"Perhaps it is time to go," suggested Mary, puzzled by her older sister's forbidding expression. "It must be very late."

It was late. It was a surprise to Lincoln to find out suddenly that the evening was over. The supper had been served with éclat and plenty of fancy food—with an abundance of oysters and ham and roast beef and salads and ices and champagne. Now it was, incredibly, three o'clock in the morning, and the guests were calling for their carriages. Everyone congratulated the bachelor hosts on a most successful cotillion.

Lincoln agreed that it had been a fine party. He had a fearful reluctance, now, to let go of the beautiful golden bubble which was that festive evening. And Mary Todd . . . Mary Todd . . . he hated seeing her go, too, hated the period lying between saying good-bye and the moment when he might see her again.

"May I see you home, Miss Todd?" he asked eagerly, but with not much hope that she would say yes. It was only a desperate grasping at any straw.

"I thank you, Mr. Lincoln," she replied primly, in her best Madame Mentelle manner, "but Mr. Edwards and my sister will escort me. It has been a most pleasant evening, sir, and a delightful party. I do thank you."

Abraham stood in the doorway and watched her depart. His heart was misbehaving, even though he had vowed he would never think of a woman again. This—this was different. Mary . . . Mary . . .

Then he half heard Elizabeth Edwards hiss to Mary:

"Whatever were you *thinking* of, Mary Todd, spending all that time with Mr. Lincoln! Don't you know he's a common, ordinary backwoodsman, doesn't know how to act in society, has no family background or connections? Don't you ever—" And her voice was lost in the distance.

Abraham turned slowly back to the hall and got his hat and coat. The joy of the party and the fun he'd had—and the inner illumination he had felt when he was with Mary Todd—were suddenly as ashes in his mouth.

Drenched in bitter loneliness, he walked slowly the long way around the square and climbed tiredly upstairs to the room he shared with Joshua Speed. Speed wasn't in yet. He was escorting his partner home, and he might be all hours getting back.

Wearily, Abraham Lincoln turned in. It was no use. He was common and he was ordinary and he was low-down and humble. He had no family, at least not the kind that counted. He had known nothing but log cabin living until he came to Springfield. Was it any wonder he didn't know how to act in society?

But people like Elizabeth Edwards would never understand or tolerate him. Ninian Edwards was like that, too. He might accept him as a constituent and appreciate his ability as a lawyer, but he was never the kind to chance inviting him home to meet his family and take supper or spend the night. But somehow, Abraham determined, he had to see Miss Todd again, even if it meant braving the high-born scorn of Elizabeth Edwards.

Mary hadn't seemed offended by him, he thought. She had really seemed to be having a right good time with him, except when he tramped on her foot, but she was lady enough to dismiss that with a smile. He wished he hadn't overheard what Mrs. Edwards had said, though, and then he wished he could have heard it all, could have listened in on just exactly what women like the fine Mrs. Edwards thought of him—and what Mary had replied. He buried his face in the pillow, groaned, turned over a couple of times in bed, which creaked under him. He thumped the pillow, and then sat up, his face against his knees. He finally lay down and was asleep before Josh Speed, shoes in hand, came quietly up the stairs and climbed in beside him.

Somehow, though, in spite of Elizabeth Edwards' objections, Mary Todd and Abraham Lincoln found many occasions in which to see each other. It was a gay winter in Springfield, with numerous parties, and the two attended nearly all of them. Abraham discovered that he felt more restless and unhappy when he was away from her than when the two were together, but she coquettishly reminded him that other men were paying court, too, and he really could not see her every evening.

"There is Mr. Webb, sir, who is coming tonight," she said one day when he was importuning her to let him call upon her in the Edwards' parlor. "And Mr. Douglas has been promised for to-morrow—he is escorting me to Mercy Levering's party. But perhaps after that—"

Being put off made Abraham all the more eager. He burned with unhappiness and anger, however, when he chanced upon Mary flirting with other gentlemen.

"I don't know what you can be thinking of," scolded Elizabeth Edwards sternly, seeing how often Mary was with Lincoln. "He is a nobody and a nothing and never will amount to anything worth while, not with his common, low background. He is awkward and ugly and doesn't know how to dress, nor how to behave with a lady. He is totally lacking in social accomplishments, Miss, and he is not helping your reputation by being seen with you so frequently. People will talk. They will say you are actually becoming serious about him! You aren't, are you?" she pried.

"Perhaps I am, Lizzie," said Mary quietly, facing her sister. There was a determined set to the Todd chin. Elizabeth, however, was also a Todd.

"Then I shall have to forbid him to enter this house!" she said coldly.

"Oh, Elizabeth!" put in Ninian Edwards indulgently as he saw tears come into Mary's blue eyes. "Let the girl alone. She won't do anything rash and neither will Lincoln. Mary knows his background and would never stoop to marrying anyone like that. If he amuses her—as I must confess he also amuses me, and the man does have sense and a certain charm—then let her play. I predict nothing will ever come of it. We are aristocrats, and Lincoln would never presume to rise above his station."

Mary said nothing more, but she set her lips in the line which was well known among the strong-willed Todds. If she wished to see Mr. Lincoln, she would see him, and whenever she liked!

The days went on, and the weeks and the months, and Lincoln was torn again between what he wanted and what he knew was best. He had come to love Mary with a deep-down, aching affection which he had never felt for any other woman.

When Abraham had proposed to Mary Owens he had fancied he was in love, but he knew now that it was not that—not if what he was feeling, night and day, for Mary Todd was the real thing. And he knew that it was. And from the way she looked at him—how she brightened as with a lovely glow when he came near her and was sad when he had to leave, with the stern eye of Elizabeth Edwards always watching—he was certain that Mary loved him.

Still, marriage—would he know how to be a husband? Did he love her enough . . . could he provide properly for her . . . what was love, anyway . . . was he really in love . . . did she love him? Night after night, he lay awake or paced, pondering. He discussed it lengthily with Joshua Speed, but resolved nothing.

It was a considerable surprise to Abraham Lincoln, therefore, that, one evening, in the elegant parlor of the Edwards' mansion, he took Mary's small, plump white hand in his big brown one and asked her to marry him.

"I know I'm nothing much to look at, or have hardly anything to offer you, Molly," he apologized, still holding the little hand as if it were all that bound him to hope and happiness. "I can't support you in the way you've been accustomed to, but I can give you a heart full of love and will be faithful all our lives together. Will you, Molly?"

"Yes, Mr. Lincoln," she said softly, looking up into his earnest gray eyes, which were so straight and level and loving and unhappy. She snuggled a bit closer. "I would live with you wherever you went and in whatever manner you lived."

No date was set for the wedding that evening.

"I shall have to plan it with Elizabeth and Frances," said Mary, inwardly quailing at the storm which she knew would rise when her news was out. "But a summer wedding would be nice, when the flowers are all in bloom and the weather fine."

And Elizabeth Edwards stormed. She threatened, and she wept. Mary was firm. She, too, stormed and she, too, on occasions, wept violently, so that the two Todd tempers clashed continually over the conflict and got quite nowhere.

"I *shall* marry him!" cried Mary desperately one day, worn to the breaking point by Elizabeth's incessant needling. "I shall, I shall, I shall! And you cannot stop me!" She fled to her room, weeping wildly, and went to bed with a blinding headache which made her so ill and nauseated that she could not eat for three days.

When she was well again, she insisted that Abraham come to call as usual. When he was let in by the little maidservant, who wore a scared look on her narrow, pinched face, he knew something was wrong. Mary was in the parlor. She attempted to be as gay as always, but it was a forced gaiety, a forced brightness of conversation, brittle and almost hysterical. There was desperation in her eyes.

Elizabeth Edwards stalked in. With a swish of her gown, she seated herself across the room from the two. Abraham could feel her eyes boring into him. His own lame conversation tapered off and he sat silently, hands between his knees, staring at the roses on the rug. Mary chattered on and on about nothing, but he scarcely heard her. At nine, he got up wearily to go.

"Good-bye, Molly," he said, with unutterable sadness, taking her hand more tightly than was needful and gazing with grief into her unhappy eyes. "Good night, ma'am," he said, looking toward Mrs. Edwards. who, unsmilingly, returned sharply:

"I bid you good night, Mr. Lincoln!"

He let himself out the big door with the frosted glass panes ornamented with flowers. The chill of that fine house had entered his soul. It had frozen him out, and he doubted if he had ever felt worse in his life.

"I can't continue like this!" he confessed in desperation to Joshua Speed, later that evening. "I'll have to break off with Molly. Maybe if I write a letter—"

"No, you've got to do it in person," reproved Speed. "It's cowardly to write a girl a thing like that. But don't be in a hurry or you'll regret it all of your life, Lincoln. I'm sure Mary Todd loves you, and you love her . . ."

"That may well be," returned Abraham bitterly. "But sure as fate, Mrs. Edwards doesn't return the affection. I even have my doubts about Mary, sometimes."

"You aren't marrying Mrs. Edwards," pointed out Speed, smiling.

"I might as well be!" retorted Lincoln unhappily. "When you marry a Todd, you marry all the kin and connections and have them on your neck for the rest of your life. I doubt if I could take it for very long."

Two days later, he passed Mary Todd and Stephen Douglas in animated conversation, riding in Douglas' fine carriage. Mary was coquetting outrageously and apparently was having a delightful time, while Mr. Douglas' face mirrored his adoration.

That night, Lincoln braved the chill of the Edwards' mansion.

"Mary," he began, with no more ado, "we simply cannot go on like this. You would be happier with—someone else—while

I, well, I cannot continue calling at a house where I am not wanted!"

It was out. He had said it. Bald though it sounded, it was the truth.

Mary's face whitened, then flushed, as if he had struck her.

"Oh, no, no, Mr. Lincoln!" she cried, beginning to weep. "You cannot be so cruel! Why, I—"

"Nothing is right; everything is going wrong," he insisted stubbornly, resisting her tears. "You have no need of me."

"But I do! Oh, please, Mr. Lincoln, I know what you are thinking —There is nothing, nothing at all, between Mr. Douglas and myself. Nothing!"

He could feel himself melting, though he fought it down. He simply must break off now and get it over with, so he could settle down and not stew and fret over what he could not have.

"I am sure—" he began stiffly, when she flung herself into his arms, which closed quite naturally around her, while she poured tears onto his vest.

That did it! Instead of getting it over with promptly and coldly, he held Mary in his arms and kissed away her tears. They spent the evening talking quietly, making plans, promising eternal devotion. The doubts he had unhappily entertained had dissolved, had become misty and unreal. He had not solved the problem of placating the Edwards-Todd clique, but he felt more certain of Mary's affection.

Christmas came and went. It was New Year's Day, 1841. Callers arrived at the Edwards' mansion, to pay their respects and to drink toasts to Mr. and Mrs. Edwards and to the coming year. Punch was ladled from a big crystal bowl by a dignified Negro manservant. There was chicken salad and there were three kinds of cake, and candies and nuts of many sorts.

Abraham Lincoln, his desperation returning, hesitated to call, even though Mary had invited him. Still, he came. After receiving a frosted stare not only from Elizabeth Edwards but from his friend, Ninian Edwards, as well, he felt he had reached the end.

Nothing, now, not tears or promises or high hopes, could change things.

"Come in here with me, Molly," he said in a low voice. "I've got to see you alone."

They went into a small sitting room, empty at the moment. She arranged her skirts around her on the sofa. He dropped into a chair which was too small for him. His face was full of tragedy and he felt almost physically ill with what he was going to have to say.

"Molly," he began hoarsely, not looking at her. "Molly—I—we—can't go on any longer like this. Hasn't it all been a mistake?" He dared a glance at her tense, white face, then dropped his eyes again.

"Your sister is dead set against me; so is Ninian, though I wouldn't have thought it of him. I guess it's different when you see your sister-in-law throwing herself away on a man who grew up in a log cabin and ate hog and hominy all his life and hasn't money or position—or anything! I can't let you do it—I've got to stop seeing you . . . you'll get over it, and maybe I will. . . ." He was floundering miserably now.

In the heavy silence that fell he looked up and found Mary with her face buried in her hands, shoulders shaking with sobs. He could not stand that. He took two long strides and pulled her to her feet.

"Don't! You mustn't, Molly!" And as she looked up with streaming eyes, he enfolded the girl hungrily in his long arms and smoothed the glossy, copper-brown curls.

They sat down on the sofa and Abraham comforted her until she had stopped her weeping.

"You don't really mean it—do you—Mr. Lincoln?" she asked, her breath catching in the sobs which still welled up inside her. "It doesn't—matter—about Elizabeth—or anything!"

"Molly—my dear, I *have* to mean it!" he groaned, laying his cheek down on her soft hair. "It won't work. And it most surely never would while I feel like this. You would be throwing away your life and your self-respect. You deserve the best, and I can only give you mediocrity. . . . Molly, I just can't go on. Let me go. Maybe later on things will be different. . . ." He really didn't expect that they would be, but he had to utter some words of hope.

She slid from his side and stood before him, small and grief-stricken, her hands tightly clenched together.

"Good-bye—Mr. Lincoln," she said, and then her voice broke and she fled from the room. He could hear her running up the carpeted stairs and heard a door slam in the distance.

Elizabeth Edwards, silently and with an ill-concealed look of triumph on her handsome face, let him out of the door. She closed it quietly and very firmly behind him.

The gloom which settled upon Abraham after what he felt was a despicable, if necessary, deed made him physically ill. He felt that his mind was slipping. He could eat but little, could not work, could only lie, weak and hopeless, in bed. His love for Mary, his impossible situation with her family and the cruel manner in which he had felt obliged to treat her raced around and around in his brain, like a rat in a cage.

Doctor Anson Henry, his good friend, attended him daily and tried to relieve his physical and mental anguish, but a doctor could do little. Still, it was a comfort and a source of some inner strength to have his beloved Doctor Henry at his bedside, to know he was coming in each day.

"I hear that your Mr. Lincoln has quite lost his mind," said Elizabeth Edwards with considerable relish. "They say he is totally insane. It is certainly sensible that you gave him up before you were tied for life to a hopeless lunatic!"

There was nothing for Abraham to do but climb out of the depression himself, to somehow evade the clammy grip of hypochondria and self-condemnation which filled him. But it was a difficult journey. So many things were happening to upset his good and settled way of life.

For, on the same day that he had broken off with Molly, Joshua

Speed had sold his store. In a few weeks, he would be moving back to Kentucky and the old family home, and Lincoln not only would be bereft of a room and companionship, but of the chance to lay his soul bare before this discreet and faithful friend, who also could, in confidence, lay forth his own soul to be comforted.

Joshua stayed by Abraham until he was well. Thinner and more hollow-cheeked, he was back at work before the end of that fatal month of January. Speed moved to Kentucky. Lincoln went to live at William Butler's comfortable home.

Mrs. Butler reminded him of some of the kind women he had known in New Salem. She mothered him, saw that his clothes were mended and that he took his umbrella when it was raining. There were children in the household, and there was nothing like a good romp with youngsters to cheer him up and chase away his blues.

It took some time, however, to get back into the full swing of work at Stuart's law office. On Lincoln's return, besides, it was very plain that John Todd Stuart was not pleased at the way his partner had neglected his work nor with the way in which he was bungling even simple cases. It hurt the firm's reputation.

Besides, John Stuart was a Todd, and the Todds stuck together. Much as he had liked Lincoln, so that he had even brought him in as a partner, this did not mean that he favored him as a relative by marriage.

If the autocratic Elizabeth Edwards, his cousin, did not want Lincoln to marry Molly Todd, then it behooved the other members of the family to uphold the situation. The other kinfolk in Springfield were doing it, standing aloof and not speaking to Mr. Lincoln unless they could not avoid it. Consequently, John Stuart had to stand behind their earnest efforts in making certain that the undesirable Mr. Lincoln did not become one of the family.

Stuart was not quite sure as to how he should do this. It was a delicate situation; besides, he still liked the fellow. If he could only get Lincoln out of Springfield.

"If you could secure for him a position of some sort *quite* far away from here," suggested Elizabeth Edwards one day, "a position with sufficient dignity, of course, so that he would want it. But do try to manage one so far distant that he would seldom or never get back to Springfield, at least so long as Mary is with us!

"Goodness knows what I shall do with the girl," she went on. "Frances was never troublesome like that. She found an excellent husband and settled down nicely, but Mary is in a dreadful state, I assure you, John. She has had several bad spells of that devastating headache from which she suffers periodically. If that man were out of town, doubtless she would come to her senses—and would feel better, besides!"

"Well, Lizzie," said John Stuart, thinking hard, "I shall see what can be done." He was remembering something Lincoln himself had said, one desperate day when everything went wrong—that he wished he could get a job far, far away and start afresh.

In March, John Stuart recommended to the Secretary of State in Washington that a certain capable Mr. A. Lincoln be appointed as *Chargé d'Affaires* in Bogota, Colombia. This was almost too good to be true, Elizabeth Edwards exulted. South America was as distant as the moon, at least so far as coming back to Springfield was concerned.

But Abraham Lincoln refused to have anything to do with the post, even if he should be approved for it.

"All right, then," said Stuart in anger, his lips tight and his usually pleasant and handsome face cold. "I should rather think that, in the light of the way in which you have neglected your work here, we shall have to dissolve this partnership."

"As you say, Stuart," replied Lincoln listlessly. There had been so many blows lately, this one failed to startle or hurt him very much. It had been extraordinarily kind of Stuart to have let him work here and gain a certain prestige by being associated with an established lawyer and aristocrat, but Abraham had always felt it was really no place for him.

However, Stephen T. Logan, who was also a prominent lawyer, invited Abraham Lincoln to become a junior partner in his firm. Lincoln thankfully moved his few belongings from Stuart's office and settled in with Logan, whom he liked and admired. Then

Stuart, wishing a partner, played it safe by taking in Benjamin Edwards, who was a brother of the estimable Ninian and brother-in-law of the determined Elizabeth.

After that, it seemed to Abraham Lincoln that the crises of his life were leveling off a bit, and maybe he would be able to live normally again. Spring burgeoned beautifully in Illinois and then early summer put the fragrance of wild strawberries among the prairie grass as Lincoln set off on the judicial circuit for a round of cases. In August, he went down to Kentucky, to visit Josh Speed and his delightful family.

It was a long trip, both coming and going, and it meant a considerable loss of fees from cases through being absent, but Abraham felt that he needed to get away; the lure of seeing Joshua again was all he required to make him set off.

It meant, too, that he would be on the rivers again, and he knew that the very presence of those ever-moving waters would restore a certain peace to his soul. He was trying his best to forget Mary Todd, and the rivers, as much as anything, might help him to do so.

He boarded a small steamboat at Beardstown and settled down happily for a journey which took him over familiar waters, beside familiar shores . . . down the Illinois, past the big cliffs, into the Mississippi and on to St. Louis.

Here he boarded a larger steamboat, a fine, fancy, white affair, with three decks and an assortment of more or less fashionable passengers. The boat made many stops, wherever a landing showed on the Mississippi's shores and someone waved to attract the pilot's attention. At last the boat turned left, into the great, broad, beautiful stream which was the Ohio River. Abraham hadn't been on the Ohio since that time so long ago when he and Allen Gentry had navigated a flatboat from Rockport, Indiana, to New Orleans. It seemed about half a century ago, but it was really only about thirteen years. When he recollected how happy and delighted he was on that trip, with the whole world before him and the rivers unroll-

IT WAS NOT A SUCCESSFUL PERFORMANCE. SHE WAS TOO SHORT FOR SO TALL A PART-NER, AND HE DIDN'T KNOW HOW TO HOLD HER PROPERLY.

THERE WAS ONE PARALYZED MOMENT IN WHICH EACH STARED AT THE OTHER. THEN,
WITH A GLAD CRY, MARY FLUNG HERSELF INTO THE LONG ARMS. . . .

ing for the first time to get him away from the backwoods, he could almost wish he was that same hopeful boy again.

Visiting at the Speed plantation was the first real vacation Abraham Lincoln had ever known. The unaccustomed experience of having Negro servants waiting on him, tasted but briefly at Madame Duchesne's home on those two trips to Louisiana, was startling, but it amazed him how quickly he became accustomed to it. The Speed slaves were happy, well cared for individuals; he could see how such as they would be content with their lot and slavery could be considered not too undemocratic an institution.

But on his return journey down the Ohio and up the Mississippi, together with Josh Speed, who had decided to go along for a visit in Springfield, Lincoln saw some other slaves who confirmed his earlier opinion of the evils of slavery. These were men and women who were being taken to New Orleans to be sold. They were chained together!

Lincoln saw them down on the lower deck, among the mules and merchandise.

"They're fastened together like fish on a trotline!" he exclaimed with disgust to Speed, who looked down, too, but evidently did not share his horror.

"They're not unhappy," Speed pointed out. "Listen: they're singing. No, they're happy enough, you may be sure."

Abraham looked at the chained Negro people, listened to their plaintive voices, and he could not believe it was right, nor that a sight such as this belonged in a free America particularly. He was in an unhappy mood all the rest of the day, and Speed could scarcely jog him out of it with his talk of the girl with whom he had finally fallen deeply in love.

This interesting topic occupied most of the long journey and continued when the pair were again in Springfield.

"I'm sure this is the real thing," Speed insisted—and sighed. "Yet how can anyone be sure? What if I made a mistake and only found out when it was too late?"

187

"You know as well as I do that you have finally located the one you love!" chided Lincoln, laughing a little at his friend. "After meeting your charming Miss Fanny Henning, with those wonderful black eyes and that devastating curly hair, I don't wonder that you feel you've found the right one at last! Why punish yourself by questioning too much and trying to analyze your feelings? Tell her you love her and want to make her your wife. I'll wager she feels the same way about you."

"You make it sound mighty simple," sighed Speed. "Just give me time, Lincoln, just give me time. When I go back home, I shall know; it will be one way or the other. That was why I wanted to get away—so I should see it all the clearer. And what about you?"

"Well, Speed," replied Abraham sadly, "I'm afraid I still feel the way I did about Molly Todd. I'd marry her in a minute if she were anyone but a Todd and an aristocrat whose family looks down on me as if I were a toad crawling in the dust. She would not be happy and neither would I. But I'm afraid—well, I just can't let myself think too much, or I'd fly off to the Edwards' stronghold and make another great blithering fool of myself. If only I were certain that she is not brooding, is not unhappy. From all I hear, however, she is going to parties again and flirting with certain eligible gentlemen whose throats I should like to cut!"

There were plenty of "kind friends" to tell Abraham that Mary Todd was going about with Edwin Webb and Stephen Douglas and certain others, openly coquetting with them. Abraham was thankful she had not gone into a decline over being jilted. As for himself, it was astonishing how the human spirit could bounce back from seemingly almost insuperable blows.

CHAPTER TWENTY

"WE *must* DO something about this dreadful situation," exclaimed Mrs. Simeon Francis over her tea. "Those two cannot go on like this, nor, I confess, can I!"

"What do you suggest, my dear?" asked Mrs. Lawrason Levering quizzically. "You know well enough how strong-minded Mary Todd is—and Lincoln is no better when he has his mind set on what he fancies is the wise course to pursue. You cannot make people like those two do something which they feel is not the right thing!"

"But why is it *not* right for them to be together again—to marry as they both must wish? Elizabeth Edwards is such a snob—and I pray that you do not run immediately and tell her I said so! Class distinction is all very well, but this is America and it is certainly a poor show of democracy to snub and ostracize an eminently good young man with an excellent future, just because his people lived in a log cabin and never amounted to a hill of beans!"

"I thought Molly was growing serious about Mr. Webb. He certainly is paying ardent court."

"Oh, how could she—he is a widower with two young children!"

"Well, just what do you propose to do, my dear?" put in gentle Mrs. Jayne, sipping her tea thoughtfully and eying Mrs. Francis closely.

"I propose to use guile and get Molly and Abraham together in the same room and let propinquity do the rest!" Mrs. Francis laughed confidently, setting her delicate china cup down on the tea table. "Now listen, this is what I want to do, and you must help me. . . ."

Julia Jayne, one of Mary Todd's best friends, paid her usual afternoon call at the Edwards' mansion and immediately went upstairs to Mary's room, so they could talk.

"Molly," began Julia, eyes sparkling with the joy of conspiracy, "just think! Mrs. Francis is planning an afternoon tea party and it will be ever so fine! All the girls of our set are to be there, and you must not fail us. Do say you can come. She gave me this invitation to deliver to you—I declare, I almost forgot it!"

She handed over the small, scented missive and Mary quickly opened and read it, her mouth curving into a delighted smile at prospect of a party. She loved parties and went to almost all to which she was invited. Yet she was growing excessively bored with importunate Edwin Webb's attentions—and even of Stephen Douglas with his sense of self-importance. This, however, would be a girls' party. It would be a relief not to have the men about . . . all but one man, and he was never at the parties which she attended now. She sighed, fingering Mrs. Francis' note.

"Well, Molly, what do you say?" urged Julia, watching her friend's changing expression and wishing she knew what Mary was thinking.

"I will go, of course," answered Mary, brightening. "Since it is only the girls, I shall not need an escort and that will be a relief! No, don't laugh, it really will. Now, what shall I wear? What are you wearing, Julie, your sprigged muslin? Perhaps I shall have to make myself a dress; I simply have nothing that is new enough. I have that length of delaine which would be just the thing, if only I have the time. Next Tuesday? Oh, surely, if I work fast!"

And the two were off on a delightful talk of clothes, while Mary brought out the dress material and hoped there was enough of it.

Meanwhile, Simeon Francis, newspaper editor, sent a note to Abraham Lincoln in his law office, where business was slow and

Logan out of town. Lincoln was sitting slumped in a chair, his feet propped on the window sill, so that only his shoe soles were visible from the street below. They were proof enough that Lawyer Lincoln was in his office, without the bother of climbing the stairs to find out.

Francis' messenger delivered the note, which read:

My dear Lincoln,
I have several problems to discuss with you which require privacy, and would be highly favored if you could find the time to come to my home on Tuesday next, about 3 o'clock, to talk them over,

and oblige,
your humble servant,
Simeon Francis

"Here, boy, take this reply back to Mr. Francis," Lincoln said to the urchin, who still waited, the bare toes of one foot curled over the arch of the other.

"I'll be there," Abraham had written, and signed it *A. Lincoln.*

"What if they don't come, after all?" worried Mrs. Francis. "What if Lincoln is called away on a case, or what if Mary gets one of those blinding headaches and cannot come either? And maybe, just maybe, they'll be furious and won't make up! Oh, dear, why do young people have to be so difficult?"

"There now, don't worry so, my dear," soothed her husband, patting her shoulder. "They'll come, and they'll thank you afterward, you see if they don't!"

Lincoln arrived promptly at three.

"Will you please have a chair in the sitting room, Mr. Lincoln?" urged Mrs. Francis, in a high state of nerves and fluttering about in a manner quite unlike her usual calm habit. "Mr. Francis was detained at the office and will be in very soon."

"Surely, ma'am," said Lincoln agreeably. "I can catch up on the news in the latest *Sangamo Journal.*"

Mrs. Francis, watching anxiously from the front window, thought Mary Todd would never, never come.

Then, suddenly, she was there at the door, and Mrs. Francis

hastily opened it and welcomed her effusively.

"How very nice to see you, Molly! Come, take off your bonnet and gloves—it is so warm, isn't it? Here is a fan—oh, you have brought your own. What a charming piece of carving in the ivory. I declare, it is quite the loveliest thing I have ever seen!"

Mary was startled at the manner in which Mrs. Francis fluttered and seemed ill at ease. She was also surprised at the quiet of the house. She was a bit late for the tea—following Elizabeth Edwards' mandate that a lady is always a little late—and expected all the girls to be assembled before her. But there was no delicious gabble of female voices, no rattle of teacups, in fact no evidence of a party at all.

"Do I have the wrong day?" she asked, puzzled.

"No, no, of course you haven't!" cried Mrs. Francis. "Come in here, do, and the rest will be along soon."

Before she could do anything about it, Mary Todd found herself in the small sitting room, facing the tall figure of Abraham Lincoln, who had dropped his newspaper and sprung to his feet when he saw her enter.

There was one paralyzed moment in which each stared at the other.

Then, with a glad cry, Mary flung herself impulsively into the long arms, which closed hungrily about her.

When Mrs. Francis, hearing nothing, cautiously opened the door a crack, sometime later, she discovered the strong-minded Mr. Lincoln seated on the sofa with the strong-minded Miss Todd—and there was the most blissful expression on both their faces.

Mrs. Francis smiled in utmost relief and pushed open the door.

"Is it all settled?" she asked happily. "Are you two going to be sensible now and be friends again?"

"Yes, ma'am, I reckon we are," Lincoln answered placidly.

Mary sat up straighter and smoothed her rumpled curls, though she was quite unflurried at being caught in such an undignified position.

"We were such fools," she said forthrightly. "I'm glad you made us come to our senses, dear Mrs. Francis. But I don't know what we shall do from now on. I cannot invite Mr. Lincoln to my sister's house. She wouldn't have it, and would likely make a scene and so should I, and there we would be, in a sad fix all over again. Oh dear, why does life have to be so hard?"

She felt tears coming to her eyes and Abraham, discovering them, reached up with his handkerchief and fondly wiped them away.

"Now don't you worry about that," said Mrs. Francis determinedly. "I'm not one to kowtow to Elizabeth Edwards. If you can find a way to get out without arousing suspicion, and if Abraham will come over here to our house, you may see each other in perfect safety and propriety, and no will be the wiser."

"Now that is what I call having a friend in need!" Lincoln smiled delightedly. "Mrs. Francis, I vote you a special medal of honor for being so kind!" He paused before adding solemnly, "Ma'am, you are provoking the wrath of the Edwards and Todd clans, than which nothing else has more fury."

He stood up, straightening his tie, then added, "But at this moment I can't think of anything I would rather provoke—all save the wrath of the particular Todd who stands before us! Bless you, ma'am!"

It was exciting, meeting in secret. Perhaps the very delight of secrecy and of outwitting Elizabeth and Ninian Edwards made the meetings all the more fun. Other friends conspired to provide meeting places also, so that Elizabeth should not wonder why her sister was visiting too frequently in one place.

But Elizabeth Edwards was only pleased that Mary was going out more often and not staying in her room so much. The girl was finally well over her infatuation for that low Lincoln creature, she concluded, and it would only be a matter of time before she decided on one of the excellent young men living in Springfield to become her husband. . . . He would be a man with money and position, of course. There were several of these, including Mr. Douglas and Mr. Webb.

Elizabeth flicked a spot of dust from the carving on the big, gold-framed mirror in the best parlor and went to reprimand the little servant girl for being slovenly in her work.

CHAPTER TWENTY-ONE

Jᴀᴍᴇꜱ ꜱʜɪᴇʟᴅꜱ was angry. His mounting fury threatened to
cause him to do something rash, and the more he thought about
the insult he had suffered, the more he boiled. He *would* have satisfaction—when he discovered the true villain, the culprit, the evil-
doer who had so grossly dishonored his name! It was more than
flesh and blood could bear, especially the Irish flesh and blood of
the furious James Shields.

It all went back to the financial panic, which really was no one
person's fault, and certainly not the fault of the state auditor, James
Shields. There was too little hard money circulating; bank notes
were being used instead, but so far had the value of the dollar
dropped that it was now worth only about forty-four cents.

James Shields, hot-tempered, black-haired, snapping-eyed Irishman that he was, as auditor set off the powder keg of public in-
dignation when he announced that, since a dollar was actually
worth only forty-four cents in buying power, in paying their taxes,
men should consider it as just that amount and pay their taxes in
silver—silver, mind you! Paper would not do.

The roar which went up was loud enough to curl the hair of
the irritable Celt, but this was nothing to what happened when
the Whigs, delighted to catch a Democrat in such an unpopular
position, began capitalizing on the situation.

Abraham Lincoln, with his facility of pen and wit, and an expert
at writing anonymous letters to the press, composed an epistle
purportedly from the "Lost Townships," located at some indeter-

minate point in Illinois. It was humorously and satirically written and was signed by someone said to be a farm widow named Rebecca.

On September 2, 1842, subscribers to the *Sangamo Journal*, which included most of the population of Springfield and Sangamon County, read and laughed in delight over "Aunt 'Becca's" piece.

"Whoever wrote it sure knows what we're up against with Shields and his hard money terms!" farmers exclaimed.

"Listen here at what she says—if it's really a *she*, which I doubt —hollerin' like a wagonload of bullfrogs about what she and her friend Jeff's had to endure:

" 'I've been tugging ever since harvest getting out wheat and hauling it to the river' (that's Jeff talkin') 'to raise State Bank paper enough to pay my tax this year, and a little school debt I owe; and now just as I've got it, I open this infernal Extra Register . . . and find a set of fellows calling themselves *officers of State* have forbidden the tax collectors and school commissioners to receive State paper at all; and so here it is, dead on my hands. I don't now believe all the plunder I've got will fetch ready cash enough to pay my taxes and that school debt.' "

"That's my idea entirely," others agreed, reading on. "But now listen to this—this sure lays into that Shields; even accuses him of bein' a Whig, and that's the highest insult you can hurl at any Democrat!"

" 'I tell you . . . there's no mistake about his bein a Whig— why his very looks shows it—everything about him shows it— if I was deaf and blind I could tell him by the smell. I seed him when I was in Springfield last winter. They had a sort of gatherin there one night among the grandees, they called a fair. All the gals about town was there, and all the handsome widows, and married women, finickin about, trying to look like gals, tied as tight in the middle and puffed out at both ends like bundles of fodder that hadn't been stacked yet, but wanted stackin pretty bad. And then they had tables all around the house kivered over with baby caps and pincushions and ten thousand little knicknacks, tryin to sell 'em to the fellows that were bowin and scrapin, and kungeerin about 'em.

" 'They wouldn't let no Democrats in, for fear they'd disgust the ladies, or scare the little gals, or dirty the floor. I looked in at the window, and there was this same fellow Shields floatin about on the air, without heft or earthly substance, just like a lock of cat-fur where cats had been fightin.

"He was paying his money to this one and that one, and tother one, and sufferin great loss because it wasn't silver instead of State paper; and the sweet distress he seemed to be in,—his very features, in the ecstatic agony of his soul, spoke audibly and distinctly— 'Dear girls, *it is distressing*, but I cannot marry you all. Too well I know how much you suffer; but do, *do* remember, it is not my fault that I am *so* handsome and *so* interesting.' "

The men laughed hard at this sally, then sobered.

"Yes, he's sure right, and if I know that Shields from reputation, he ain't goin' to take all them slurs layin' down. You wait. There'll be more'n cat fur flyin'. There's ructions comin' up soon, or I miss my guess, like the feller said who dropped a powder charge down the well."

Meanwhile, several days after this entertaining effusion appeared in the public press, a second letter came out which was even more insulting. In this the stout Rebecca proposed marriage to the estimable Mr. Shields, who had, immediately after publication of the first letter, loudly voiced his dislike for the affair. Rebecca then challenged him to a duel. In the paper, a few days later, there appeared a poem which was signed "Cathleen," in which the writer caused Mr. Shields to marry the rural Rebecca.

With the offending sheet of the *Sangamo Journal* clutched in his fingers, James Shields stalked down to the newspaper office and confronted the editor, Simeon Francis.

Mr. Francis put down his cigar and sat up in his chair as the fire-breathing Shields burst into the office. Around him was an aura of insulted dignity and righteous fury.

"*If* you please, *Mr.* Francis (only he pronounced it Frauncis) you will be telling me who is the blackguard who has dared to write this calumny about me!"

"Mr. Shields! Do sit down. Now talk calmly, and we'll straighten this out—"

"I will not sit down and we will straighten it out now, at once, and standing up, or I shall demand satisfaction from you, instead of from the bounder who wrote this piece of infamy! Look at it. Read it! But no, you have already looked at it and have read it, all three pieces of insult, and no doubt laughed and have had the nerve, the insulting audacity, to print it in your worthless rag!"

James Shields threw the paper on Francis' desk and ran his fingers through his black hair, which stood straight up in wild tufts in his agitation. He paced.

"Well, now, Mr. Shields—"

"Who wrote it? That is all I ask. The name of the blackguard! The first screed was bad, but this one is worse, more vilely insulting, and as for this so-called poem—I *will* know!"

Simeon Francis knew when he was cornered. A newspaper editor has to face such a situation every once in a while and must learn to accept it with dignity and aplomb, even when the ax is falling.

"Well, sir, I regret to use his name because he is a very worthy gentleman and a constituent of yours—"

"Even if he were my own brother, which I thank God he never will be, I would want his name that I may challenge him for satisfaction. Out with it!"

"Abraham Lincoln is the author of the *Rebecca* letter which appeared September 2—"

"Lincoln!" Shields interrupted savagely. "I might have known! He's a sly one with the pen and skilled in the use of words . . . words to run a man through and through, and then he has not the courage to sign his name like a man. Lincoln! I'll cut his heart out!" Shields was off, coattails flying.

And Simeon Francis, who knew that Lincoln had written only one of the letters, mopped his brow and sank back into his chair.

Lincoln had already departed for the circuit court sessions at Tremont, about sixty-five miles north of Springfield, near Pekin.

This, however, was no deterrent to the raving Mr. Shields. He hurried to the home of his friend, General John D. Whiteside.

"You must be my second, general!" Shields gasped. "I'm going after that scurrilous Lincoln and challenge him to a duel!"

Grasping the puzzled general's arm, he urged him to come at once, but was prevailed upon to wait until that gentleman should don his coat, arrange his stock, put on his hat and explain to his startled family where he was going, before the two set out at a gallop, heading toward Tremont.

Simeon Francis came to the door of his newspaper building in time to see Shields and Whiteside tear off in a cloud of dust. Terribly worried, he was about to re-enter his office when Dr. Elias Merryman and William Butler chanced to walk by. Both were good friends of Lincoln, who lived at the home of the latter, besides.

"Why, what's the trouble, Francis?" they asked almost in unison, seeing the editor's perturbed face.

"Oh, trouble enough and it's mainly my fault. No telling what those fools will do! Lincoln wrote that crazy piece about Shields—you read it, I'm sure; everybody did—and now the fellow is wild to cut out Lincoln's heart, he says. He's going to challenge him to a duel, of all things!"

"A duel! But that's forbidden by Illinois statute!"

"I know it is, but they'll find a way out of it, and with the state of mind Shields is in, I doubt if the law would bother him much, for all that he's a member of the Illinois governing body. He's liable to lose his post if he goes through with this. If there were only some way of warning Lincoln!"

"There is!" exclaimed William Butler with determination. "Come on, Merryman, get your horse. We'll send word to our families and be off. I know a short cut and, if we ride all night, we can get to Tremont first!"

The night was warm and humid, alive with the grand chorus of the last of summer's insects, zinging and jingling in the dusty weeds and in the tall prairie grass that waved against the stars. The galloping horses were finally slowed to a walk. At a halfway point, they were exchanged for fresh mounts. Shortly afterward,

Butler and Merryman passed two riders in the darkness. They were Shields and Whiteside, who evidently did not recognize the men who slipped by them in the summer night.

By dawn, Butler and Merryman had reached Tremont. They hunted up Lincoln's room at the ramshackle inn and pounded on the door until he woke.

"Bill and Elias!" Lincoln thrust out one hand to greet them and smoothed back his rumpled hair with the other.

"Come in, come in. You're mighty early, but take me as I am. Why, what's wrong, boys?" he added, suddenly uneasy.

"He's coming to get you—Shields!" cried Butler, sinking onto a chair. "He's taken exception to what you wrote, and he's got his second, and they're heading up here to challenge you to a duel. A duel—as if this were medieval times and a duel was the only way in which civilized men could settle their differences!"

"You really ought to watch what you write sometimes, Lincoln," reproved Dr. Merryman wearily. "It's a wonder this has not happened before. I looked for something like it when you were writing those anonymous 'Sampson's Ghost' letters for the paper. In a way, I don't blame poor Shields. You really were mighty insulting, especially that poem which came out today, not to mention the second of the letters. You really don't know the power of your pen!"

Lincoln stopped where he was, pulling on his pants.

"I only wrote one," he said, startled. "You say there was one in today?"

"And yesterday, too. A humdinger. It suggests that 'Aunt Becca' might challenge Shields to a duel and asks if *he'd* like to put on petticoats or have *her* dress in breeches, either one serving to make them equal! Today's was a poem announcing the glad tidings of a marriage between said 'Aunt Becca' and Mr. Shields. I hear he's pretty wrought up, and frankly I don't blame him!"

"Boys," said Lincoln soberly, "I swear I didn't write more than one, and it came out on September second."

"Whoever wrote the others, then?"

Lincoln sank back on his bed and looked dismally into space.

A horrid thought had just entered his mind.

"I should have thought Molly'd have had better sense, but she's so impetuous and never thinks—"

"Molly? You don't mean to tell me that Miss Todd wrote— that?"

Lincoln groaned and put his head in his hands.

"She and her friend, Julia Jayne, were laughing about the first effusion I was fool enough to write and they said it ought to be a series. I said one was enough, but I knew they were whispering and laughing about something Mary was composing . . . Oh, golly! And now you say Shields—"

"He's on his way here with blood in his eye and a second to make the challenge good and proper, to the death!"

There was an imperative rap on the door. Butler, a trifle pale, opened it a crack. General John Whiteside stood stiffly outside. In his hand was a letter.

"Please to present this letter to Mr. Lincoln, sir," he said formally, after a brief bow, though Whiteside and Butler were old friends.

"Thank you, sir," returned Butler, equally as stiffly. "I shall do so at once." He closed the door and Whiteside walked away. He was thankful he hadn't had to face Lincoln. This was all a bad business. He felt extraordinarily unhappy about it.

Wordless, Bill Butler handed the note to Lincoln, who opened it and read in silence:

. . . While abstaining from giving provocation, I have become the object of slander, vituperation and personal abuse . . .

I will take the liberty of requiring a full, positive and absolute retraction of all offensive allusions used by you in these communications, in relation to my private character and standing as a man, as an apology for the insults conveyed in them.

This may prevent consequences which no one will regret more than myself.

Your Ob't serv't,
James Shields.

"I didn't intend slander, and I'm not going to apologize for something I didn't calculate I was doing, and anyway, I didn't write all he alludes to!" snapped Lincoln. "Here, take this letter back to the dutiful Mr. Whiteside and convey my message that I will not retract anything I wrote!"

"Oh, now Lincoln, you know what will happen—" begged Bill Butler.

"All right, then, let it happen," said Lincoln curtly, finishing his dressing and giving his hair a cursory combing before the speckled mirror.

Back came James Shields' stiff letter, requiring that Lincoln select the weapons.

"Well, that's that," he said sadly. "I reckon it's up to me to choose what we shall kill each other with. I might suggest cowdung at five paces, but I suppose my worthy opponent wants something a little more formal and dangerous. Well, make it cavalry broadswords. They're the biggest weapons I can think of, off hand. And—now let me think. A plank ten feet long and nine to twelve inches wide must be laid on the ground as a boundary over which neither of us shall step."

Lincoln paused, pondering. "I reckon we'll have to get out of Illinois for this little picnic, since it is a highly illegal form of entertainment, I've been told. So why not make it that island down below Alton, the one they call Bloody Island because other fools have dueled there before us?"

"When?" asked Butler. His face was drawn with weariness and despair at this unutterably foolhardy project. He thought Lincoln was taking it all too lightly.

"Well, I'll be occupied here for a while. Say, September 22, about five in the afternoon."

Before Butler and Merryman finally went back to Springfield, a day or so later, a thought occurred to Butler.

"You know, Lincoln, it's just come to me—if you figure on fighting across a plank with weapons as long as cavalry broadswords, and with that extraordinarily long reach of yours—why,

Shields won't have the ghost of a chance to even touch you, short as he is!"

"Yes, I figured on that," said Lincoln drily, grinning a crooked grin. "That way I can disarm the fellow, and he won't accomplish what he obviously wishes—to run me through and through. I hate cruelty, especially when it's to myself!"

When the Tremont session was over, Abraham returned disconsolately to Springfield and to his fate at the hand of the insulted auditor. The whole thing was a sorry mess, and he wished he hadn't become involved in it. He wished he'd had the sense to watch how he wrote. Ever since he'd penned the *Chronicles of Reuben*, back in Indiana, and had infuriated the Grigsby clan, who had fought him because of it, he had been getting into trouble with his writing. He ought to learn better some day. Better still, he ought to quit writing!

There was nothing to do now but go through with it. Shields was still unappeased and breathing fire; he was evidently marking time with unabated wrath until the fatal day arrived.

Lincoln had only a brief moment with Mary before setting off with his friends, by horse and buggy, to Alton.

"Oh my poor Mr. Lincoln!" Mary wept, clutching his strong hands in her small white ones. "It's all my fault!"

"Don't worry, sweetheart," he said gently. "I'll be back!" Not trusting himself to say more or to stay longer, and with a quick farewell kiss, he was off.

"He is my knight, my champion going to battle for my honor," Mary sighed to Mrs. Francis and Julia Jayne, half in grief, half in pride and romantic delight.

"It's like a novel, isn't it?" mused Julia dreamily.

"It is nothing of the sort!" snapped Mrs. Francis, out of patience with both of them. "You are a pair of silly, ridiculous, sentimental geese! I know you wrote those two dreadful pieces; they were the ones that really set off this whole regrettable affair. You ought to be ashamed!

"And of course," went on Mrs. Francis furiously, "you know that Mr. Shields and General Whiteside may be arrested and lose their state jobs because of this, and Mr. Lincoln and his friends may very likely be arrested, too, and thoroughly disgraced. And your precious Mr. Lincoln may be killed, and all because of a pair of silly girls who thought they were smart!"

Julia and Mary were suddenly sobered. Each went home in thoughtful silence.

The duel was the subject of conversation in almost every home in Springfield that night. People were shocked, scandalized, amused, scornful, or otherwise concerned over two men who were very definite personalities, either of whom would be sadly missed should he fall victim to the other's swordsmanship.

"It's just like that Mr. Lincoln to become involved in a brawl like this," Elizabeth Edwards sneered at dinner. Her fine eyes glinted scorn in the candlelight. "A common, low—"

"Well, now," put in Ninian Edwards humorously, though with a trace of embarrassment. "There is a rather curious angle to it, you know, my dear." He paused. Mary and Elizabeth looked at him. Each was thinking quite different thoughts.

"I believe," went on Ninian Edwards, "that only a *gentleman* may be challenged to a duel, or even be permitted to fight one."

Again he paused, and the women listened.

"Our own opinion of that Lincoln fellow may be quite unaltered as to whether or not he is fit to have the title of gentleman, but evidently the worthy Mr. Shields and the honorable General Whiteside have no doubts in the matter. Puts one rather on a spot, you know. A man can scarcely be a gentleman and still be of such low degree that he cannot be admitted into the best homes!"

"That's what I have always said—" Mary broke in eagerly.

"Hush, Mary!" ordered Elizabeth sternly. "You know nothing about it. I still say that Mr. Lincoln is a common, low plebian who is not fit to enter the home of an aristocrat. I should never have permitted him to call on Mary, never!"

Ninian smiled and said nothing more. Mary turned her eyes to her plate, picked at her food, then, excusing herself, fled to her room.

"You don't suppose that girl is still fancying herself in love with that awful man, do you, Mr. Edwards?"

"How should I know what goes on in the head of a Todd female?" countered Ninian Edwards noncommittally. "I wouldn't be surprised at anything they do!"

On September 22, 1842, Lincoln, with his friends, Dr. Merryman and Dr. Henry, William Butler and Albert Bledsoe, arrived at Bloody Island and tied their boat to a snag. Lincoln at once set about practicing with the huge sword which he had acquired in Jacksonville. After a few minutes of awkward thrusting and parrying in the air, the pursuit seemed suddenly ridiculous. He decided to put the big blade to better use and industriously cleared away the weeds and underbrush to permit a clearer field of battle. As Shields, Whiteside and a doctor rowed across the Mississippi to the island, they could see the tall figure swinging the broadsword like a scythe, while the horseweeds, smartweeds, willow sprouts and cocklebur plants flew in all directions. Shields and Whiteside simply looked at each other and said nothing. In silence, the three landed.

"I reckon we'll have to change the rules a bit about a plank," said Lincoln, when the seconds got together to set the stage for the duel. The mosquitoes annoyed them. "I clean forgot to bring one along. I reckon a long stick of driftwood will do as well. We'll set it up on two forked sticks, like this, and it'll do as a boundary just as well as a plank. Well, I reckon we're ready, more's the pity, as the King of France said when they were about to behead him!"

The two opponents sat down on driftwood logs at a distance from each other while the seconds desperately continued trying to conciliate them and call off the fight. Lincoln was willing enough to do this, if he could do so in honor, but Shields was stubborn. Only blood would satisfy him, it seemed. Even his friends had all but lost complete patience with his bullheadedness.

Arguments got nowhere. The September heat grew greater as the afternoon moved on toward the appointed hour of five. A vast glitter rose from the flowing waters of the Mississippi. Lincoln wished he was on it, going down to New Orleans . . . anyplace but here on this baking sand bar, waiting to find out if he was going to have to fight with a great sword. Shields was said to be an expert swordsman, but Lincoln had never fought with anything more deadly than his fists.

He moved restlessly over to a shadier log under the willows. He examined the sword blade and picked off some bits of green adhering from his weed-cutting operations. He tested the blade with his thumb, then stood up, reached as high as he could with the weapon and clipped off a willow twig which dropped lightly at his feet. General Whiteside, observing this, nudged Shields.

"Did you see that, Shields? You haven't a chance with that fellow—look at his reach! He cut off a twig at least twelve feet above the ground—I tell you, this is murder!"

A St. Louis-bound steamboat navigated slowly past, dodging sand bars bared in the low water. The people on board waved to the men on the island. Lincoln was the only one who waved back. He emphasized the gesture with the great sword, which flashed in the sunshine. Suddenly remembering what it was and what he was here for, he stopped waving and sank back on his log again, sighing. Just then, his eyes fell casually on something red lying among the weeds. He got up to investigate.

"Good heavens, Henry," cried a woman on the steamboat, "did you see what that man had in his hand? A sword!"

"Oh, surely not, Maria. Must have been a fisherman and his pole."

"It was not! I think I know a fishing pole when I see one, and that man had a sword. A great long one. And come to think of it, there was another man over there with a sword, too. What on earth do you think they were going to do?"

"Fight a duel, most likely, Maria. That's what swords are for. Ah, me, I well remember the day . . ."

"All right, gentlemen," Dr Merryman finally said in despair. "Take your places and—"

A halloo from the water announced another skiff which was hastily being rowed out from shore to the island. Aboard was John J. Hardin, a lawyer, Mary Todd's cousin. Having learned of the folly about to take place, he had come in all haste to Alton and down to Bloody Island to avert disaster.

His refreshing presence spiced with strong epithets sizzling with scorn and volatile argument, finally convinced the principals of their folly. Lincoln's formal apology was read to the placated Shields. He had, in fact, been about to relent when Hardin's explosive presence crystallized his intent.

Abraham squashed a viciously-biting horsefly on his neck and wiped off the blood.

"Reckon that's the only blood that'll be shed on this field of battle, thank fortune," he remarked to no one in particular. Then a wicked light came into his eyes as he remembered the bit of an old red shirt which he had discovered lying in the weeds.

Shields and his party made ready to go back in one boat, Lincoln and his relieved friends in another. But Shields was puzzled by what the irrepressible Lincoln was up to. He was tenderly wrapping the old red shirt around a chunk of driftwood and placing it in his boat. And then, during the entire journey back to shore— a shore lined with people awaiting the outcome of the duel and straining their eyes against the late sunlight—he crouched over and solicitously fanned the red-clad log.

"Look!" cried someone on shore. "One of them's been almost killed—maybe he's dead! He's a mass of blood, anyway, just a-layin' in the bottom of the boat!"

James Shields felt himself beginning to boil again as Lincoln, grinning widely, heard the exclamations of horror turn to roars of relieved laughter. The bystanders had discovered the joke. The duel had turned into a farce and everyone, except perhaps the scarlet-faced Mr. Shields, was delighted. Mrs. Edwards, however, would have said that it was what you could expect from a boor like Lincoln.

"You'll have him challenging you to another duel before you even get back from this one," reproved Dr. Merryman, throwing log and red shirt into the river.

Meanwhile, Mary Todd and Julia Jayne were having a terrible time of it. Mrs. Francis' scalding words had brought home to them the true meaning of what they had done and what was now about to take place. Those several days, Julia spent a good deal of time with Mary in the latter's bedroom.

"Oh, what on earth have we done!" Mary had cried when they were alone. Julia sank to the floor and burst into a flood of tears. She buried her face in Mary's voluminous muslin skirts.

"It's our fault," wept Julia. "If Mr. Lincoln is killed, we'll be the same as murderers! Murderers! How I wish we had never written those shameful pieces! Mr. Francis would never, never have told Mr. Shields we wrote them, and neither would Mr. Lincoln. He would give his life for our honor. Oh, oh, oh!" Julia sobbed.

"Hush, Julie," hissed Mary fiercely, absently running her fingers through her friend's curls. "There's nothing to do about it now except pray that they don't have the fight. Maybe something will come up to stop them. My cousin, Mr. Hardin, is on his way there to see what he can do. But oh, a duel . . . oh, Julia, you are right, we *are* the same as murderers! And even though Mr. Lincoln isn't a swordsman, he is so tall and so strong, he could kill Mr. Shields with one blow of that dreadful weapon!"

The horrid thought which this brought to their minds was sickening and terrifying, and they both wept together once more.

And so at last Abraham Lincoln came home to Springfield after the barely averted duel. Julia Jayne contrived to notify Mary Todd of the event. Just by chance, then, the latter paid a call at the Francis' home.

As Abraham came striding up the front walk, alive and well, Mary forgot the polite reticence of young Victorian ladies before they were married and flew into his arms.

"Oh, Mr. Lincoln, you're safe, you're safe!" she cried, weeping happily against his flowered waistcoat. "I'm so terribly sorry about what I did. It was all my fault! But you—oh—did you—kill Mr. Shields?" she asked suddenly, wide-eyed, as the thought occurred to her that, customarily, when one man who was a party to a duel was seen alive afterward, his opponent usually was quite dead, or at least injured. She remembered certain nerve-shattering episodes involving duels in Kentucky.

"No, Molly, I didn't kill anything bigger than a horsefly that bit my neck, nor shed anyone's blood but my own in the mosquitoes that were devouring me alive! It's all over, and let's neither one of us write anything unkind or unsigned again!"

He picked her up and kissed her, then set her down, lingeringly. They went into the house together.

"Would you have been so sad if I'd been slaughtered by that furious Irishman? His sword was almost as big as he was, and mighty deadly," Lincoln added, as they reached the haven of the Francis' parlor. It was, with intent, quite empty.

"Yes, Mr. Lincoln, I would," she answered demurely, dimpling, looking down, though her heart was pounding furiously at his nearness.

"Well, so would I, I reckon. Molly, let's not fool around and get into arguments or endanger our very lives by being apart! I just can't live without you, and I flatter myself you can't live without me, else you'd have married someone richer and handsomer than I am before now. Will you marry me, Molly?"

Somehow, all the reasons why he should not marry a Todd, all the arguments he had used to convince himself of his inferiority, his poverty and his hopeless future faded into the unimportant background in the presence of the girl he loved.

"Yes, Mr. Lincoln," she whispered. His embrace was big and warm and all-engulfing, there in the Francis' parlor. She came out of the embrace pink and mussed and happier than she could ever remember being in all her tempestuous life.

CHAPTER TWENTY-TWO

IT WAS NOT UNTIL November that Mary Todd finally got up the courage to tell Elizabeth and Ninian Edwards that she was going to marry Abraham Lincoln. She was revolted by the thought of the storm which would surely break around her when her news was out. But she would have to do it.

"Molly," Abraham had said one day, "we can't go on like this much longer, seeing each other in secret, just putting off the day. We'll have to tell Mrs. Edwards and be done with it."

"I know, I know," replied Mary, feeling cornered. "I really will."

"I've written to your father for permission, but have heard nothing from him," went on Lincoln, frowning. "We won't need a big wedding, though I know you'd like it, I reckon. But with the way things are, I don't see how we can. We could just go over to Doctor Dresser's parsonage and have him marry us quietly and with no fanfare. Then let the storm break!"

"Yes, that would be best, I suppose," sighed Mary. "But I would have to tell Elizabeth beforehand. She would never forgive me if I should be married secretly like that, and Ninian, besides, is my guardian."

"Yes, you would have to," he agreed. "And I cannot do it for you!"

So, on the morning of November 4, 1842, Mary said boldly at breakfast, though her heart was hammering:

"Mr. Lincoln and I are going to be married this evening."

If she had announced the ending of the world, the shock could scarcely have been worse for her kin.

Elizabeth dropped her egg spoon, and Ninian simply stared across the damask cloth at the flushed, pretty, panicky, determined face of his sister-in-law. So she had done it, after all. He ought to have known you can't cross the will of a Todd and get away with it.

"I refuse to permit it!" cried Elizabeth, her face red. "I will not let you throw yourself away on a man with no family, no background, no money, no prospects! It would never do!"

"Yes, it will," said Mary, determining to be calm, "and I shall. We have already bought the license, and Mr. Lincoln has the ring. There are three lovely words engraved inside the band: *Love Is Eternal*. That means that nobody can stop our marriage, not even you, Elizabeth Todd, nor you, Mr. Edwards! I refuse to let you run or ruin my life. Goodness knows you've tried!"

"I have *not* tried to ruin your life, you spiteful minx," screamed Elizabeth, while the little servant girl paused, wide-eyed, in the doorway, aghast at the commotion among the grandees. "All my life I have tried to do the best for you that I could, ever since our mother died, and it devolved on me as the eldest to see that you were educated and brought up as a lady, met the right people and married the right man! I refuse to—"

"It won't make any difference what you refuse, Elizabeth," cried Mary hotly. "I am going to marry Mr. Lincoln today. At Mr. Dresser's house!"

With that, she got up from the table and, considering her agitated state of mind, walked quietly out of the room.

Elizabeth and Ninian sat back and stared at each other.

"You might as well give in, Mrs. Edwards," said her husband wryly. "You can't make a Todd do what she doesn't want to do, as I've learned long since. Give her your blessing and don't throw it up to her that she's made a dreadful match. It might be that she could have done much, much worse."

Elizabeth calmed down somewhat. "We can't let that girl go off to the Episcopalian parsonage and be married, as if we wouldn't give her a proper wedding here. It would cause talk," she cried, thinking fast.

"She seems determined to be married today, and you would scarcely have time to get a wedding supper ready, and all the decorations," Ninian Edwards told his wife.

"Oh, that girl!" cried Elizabeth petulantly. "I have always had trouble with her headstrongness! She might at least have given me time to do the proper thing by her, plan a really nice spread, order flowers and ices, invite the right people. As social leader of Springfield, they expect me to do the correct thing. Think what people will say!"

"You hardly gave her the chance, did you?" reminded Ninian. "I shall go at once and tell Lincoln that all is forgiven and they are to have the wedding here. I had a letter from Robert Todd, saying that Lincoln had written to him, asking Mary's hand in marriage. Your father will abide by my decision, he says, as to whether this man is worthy. It seems, however, that they are determined to marry whether I approve or not! Ah, well."

But Elizabeth, in a softened mood, was off to confer with Mary, who found her sister surprisingly kind after the blowup and hard words.

The wedding would still be held on that day. Elizabeth, in a flurry, sent for her other sister, Frances Todd Wallace, who came in a great state of upset. They worked hard, recruited cousins and neighbors to assist, sent invitations here and there, while Mary asked Julia Jayne, Elizabeth Todd and Anna Rodney, three of her very best friends, to be bridesmaids. There was no time for special gowns to be made for the wedding. Mary herself had had no chance to make her wedding gown, but had to wear her best white silk. The others simply wore their nicest winter dresses for the occasion.

Rain commenced about noon. This further complicated the hasty running about from house to house, to borrow things, send messages and invitations. The streets were thick mud, the rain congealing a little on the trees.

Lincoln, feeling somewhat in a daze, made the arrangements with the Reverend Mr. Dresser and asked James Matheny to stand up with him that evening at the wedding.

Meanwhile, Elizabeth and Francis mixed the wedding cake batter; it baked beautifully and did not fall. It had to be frosted before it was quite cold, but nobody minded. Everyone that evening commented on how delicate it was, how velvety and up to Elizabeth Edwards' usual standards for wedding cakes.

Rain was clattering at a slant against the long windows of the Edwards' parlor when the marriage service took place—the service which caused Mary Todd to become Mrs. Abraham Lincoln.

It was over at last, with no slip-ups. In the November rain, which somehow contrived to have bright sparkles of joy shot through it, Mr. and Mrs. Lincoln, later that evening, drove to the Globe Tavern, where a room had been reserved and where they were to live.

Elizabeth Edwards sank, worn out, into a chair and wept a little. Ninian Edwards poured himself a stiff drink. And Mr. and Mrs. Simeon Francis, driving home in the rain, drew a gratified sigh of relief.

"Congratulations, Mrs. Francis," said her husband with a smile, pressing her hand. "I think we may safely take credit for a most worthy deed!"

CHAPTER TWENTY-THREE

NINETEEN YEARS LATER, on February 11, 1861, another cold winter rain, but without the sparkles and without the joy, slanted miserably upon the gray, wet, muddy lawns and streets of Springfield. At the Great Western station, a locomotive with a baggage car and one passenger car draped with water-soaked bunting stood waiting. Bobbing umbrellas covered the people who had gathered quietly that morning, on the station platform and in the street.

At five minutes before eight, a tall man walked hastily through the crowd and mounted the back platform of the passenger car. Removing his tall hat, he stood bareheaded, his hands gripping the cold iron of the wet railing. His face was full of melancholy, his mind suddenly far away, remembering.

The engine tooted a warning. He lifted his head, then, and spoke a few words in farewell to his friends and neighbors.

"*My friends*," said President-Elect Abraham Lincoln, "*no one, not in my situation, can appreciate my feeling of sadness at this parting.*"

It was a parting from his whole life which had gone before, as if this were dying, and he were entering a new existence. Whether it would be good or ill he could not know. It was a separating from the old way of living, from the old friends, the old times.

He was leaving not only Springfield and the career he had built there for himself, as a lawyer with Stuart, then Logan, and lately with William Herndon—the career as a circuit court lawyer and a member of the State Legislature in Illinois, and as congressman in

Washington. He was leaving more than that.

He was departing from the fine house which he had purchased from Doctor Dresser, the Episcopalian minister who had married him and Molly. It was a home and a way of life, a degree of elegance, which he had never known so intimately before. It had been his beloved Mary who had spurred him to live better and more fully. It was a long way indeed from New Salem, and from a cabin in Kentucky, which had no floor and no door or windows, far from a small boy who had been whipped for asking questions.

He was leaving New Salem, too—but no, New Salem had left him. Long since, the village which had done so much for him had vanished. When he went over to say a few choked words at the burial services of his dear old friend, Squire Bowling Green, he had been horribly depressed by the devastation and death of that which had once been the village where he had lived.

There had been scarcely anything left. The ruins of the Rutledge tavern still stood, part of the carding mill, half a dozen fallen-down buildings and only gaping foundation holes where the rest had been taken away. Tall grass and weeds grew unrestrained over the ghost town. The sight had sickened him and he wanted never to return. There was nothing now to bring him back.

He had traveled again to Coles County, several weeks ago, to see his stepmother, Sarah Bush Lincoln, before going to Washington. His father was dead and so was his stepbrother, Jack Johnston. But Sarah was there, secure and calm and good, beautiful in her old age. In spite of Jack's attempts to sell her property, Abraham had kept his promise and had seen that she was cared for in comfort. She was old and thin and bent, but a sort of inner light shone from her fine, large eyes. She had held both his strong hands in her frail but capable ones and had cried a little. They had talked for a long time, and she had fixed him dinner. She was proud of his great honor, she said, but then, she had always been proud of him.

He had visited around with the relatives and neighbors, but spent little time with them. It was Sarah he wanted to be with. She was that link which took him back and back, eons away, to the Indiana cabin after his own mother had died . . . and the dim memory of

Nancy Lincoln was the link which carried him again to Kentucky
. . . and on and on in time until he could grow dizzy thinking of it.

*"To this place and the kindness of these people I owe every-
thing."*

That was not just a pretty sentiment. It was true. All these people, all those of the past . . . Caleb Hazel showing him the wild
things . . . Josiah Crawford and Judge Pitcher loaning him books
. . . Allen Gentry, Denton Offutt, Mentor Graham, Squire Green,
James Rutledge, Joshua Speed, the people who had voted him four
times into the Legislature and once to the United States Congress
. . . John Stuart who had helped him become a lawyer . . . Mary
Todd Lincoln who loved him and had confidence in what he did
and what he could do . . . they had done this thing, not he.

*"Here I have lived for a quarter of a century, and have passed
from a young to an old man."*

It was curious to think of the passage of time and what it could
do to a man. As if he stood a long way off, he could remember an
unworried, ignorant youth who, nearly thirty years ago, led by
some strange and guiding impulse, came down the Sangamon River
to work at odd jobs in New Salem. A youth with no special talents,
aims or purposes in life . . . he could scarcely relate him to the
tired individual who stood on a train platform in the rain, saying
good-bye to the people who had bestowed upon him the doubtful
honor of the presidency of the United States. He was only fifty-one
years old, but he felt very aged indeed, with the gray winter rain
pouring over the landscape and oppressing his soul.

"Here my children have been born, and one is buried."

Ah, his dear, dear boys! They were enough to make him young
again. He had always loved children, and when he and Mary had
had their first baby, had held their precious Bobby in their arms, he
had never felt his life so full, so wonderful and so meaningful as it
was then.

It had been fuller than ever when Eddie was added to the family,
now living in the fine house on Eighth Street. But he still inwardly
wept when he remembered how Eddie, at four years, had fallen ill
and no one could save his life. He had thought that his darling

Mary would die, too, so great was her anguish. But then God had given them Willie and Tad to ease the grief of loss. He hated going away and leaving the little one in his grave out in Hutchinson's Cemetery.

"I now leave, not knowing when, or whether ever, I may return,"

He had told William Herndon just the day before, with tears very close to the eyes of both men, to keep the sign up, the one that said LINCOLN AND HERNDON; because, if he lived, he would be back some day and they could take up their practice where they had left off. He wished heartily, with a sudden revulsion in his soul, that he were not going, after all. He was sick of the job already and shuddered at what lay ahead.

"with a task before me greater than that which rested upon Washington."

He had always had tasks before him . . . the endless jobs of chopping firewood for his mother, of splitting rails for his father and the neighbors, or to pay for a poor, homespun suit of clothes— a thousand fence rails to buy a suit which did not fit. He had had tasks of physical strength, like fighting the Mississippi River or neighborhood bullies; or of taming the forest for a cabin and a garden patch; and there had been tasks of the mind which were infinitely harder.

He would still be a manual laborer, a riverman, a farmer, a woodcutter, with a placid existence and few worries except those of death and taxes, if his mind had not driven him to the tasks before him. Tasks like wresting an education out of nothing; of learning river navigation and surveying; how to be a captain in the Illinois militia, and how to bury men killed by Indians. They had been tasks like law and mathematics, grammar, manners and judgment; and the wisdom of dealing with men, and of using his deep inner compassion to guide him when even his keen, analytical mind did not always direct the true course.

But those had been small tasks compared with what lay ahead. Before him lay the government of a nation which was disturbed with hatred over issues which might not be settled peaceably, issues which could split open and destroy the land that George Washington and the founding fathers had created with such love, thought and precision. It was, appallingly, going to be up to him—to plain, fumbling, uncertain Abraham Lincoln—no Washington, he—to keep America whole, strong and safe forever. It was too much for mortal man. Still—

"Without the assistance of that Divine Being Who ever attended him, I cannot succeed. With that assistance, I cannot fail."

Within him rose again the deep conviction of the goodness of God and the rightness of the destinies He guided, and a certain calm power flowed into him.

"Trusting in Him who can go with me, and remain with you, and be everywhere for good, let us confidently hope that all will yet be well. To His care commending you, as I hope in your prayers you will commend me, I bid you an affectionate farewell."

A puffing locomotive drawing two bunting-draped cars moved off into the gray slants of bitter February rain, which drenched the already sodden Sangamon country, and headed east toward Washington.

VIRGINIA S. EIFERT

has lived all her life in Springfield, Illinois, the heart of the Lincoln country. As a natural outgrowth of this association, we now have her fourth book about Abraham Lincoln, entitled *With a Task Before Me*. This carries the Lincoln story from 1832 to 1861 and his departure for the White House, continuing a narrative which began in *The Buffalo Trace* with the indomitable Lincoln grandparents in 1780. This book won the New York *Herald Tribune* Award in 1955 and the Thomas Edison Foundation Award in 1956. Chronologically there followed *Out of the Wilderness* and *Three Rivers South. With a Task Before Me* is the fourth.

Mrs. Eifert, mother of an eleven-year old son, is editor of the monthly magazine, *The Living Museum*, issued by the Illinois State Museum, and author of *Mississippi Calling*, a nonfictional biography of the big river, the people whom it influenced or who attempted to influence it, from 9,000 B.C. to the present. To obtain material for this comprehensive work, the author traveled more than 5,500 miles on Diesel towboats up and down the Mississippi, seeing firsthand the diverse character of the river.